Chickens & Stuff

The Complete Anthology

Contributors —

Samantha Biggers, Katelynn Bond, Jill Bong, Jackie Clay-Atkinson, Kenny Coogan, Nell Davidsen, Dotty DeVille, Allen Easterly, Carol Frieberg, Karen House, Donna Insco, James Kash, Amanda Kemp, Brad Rohdenburg, Habeeb Salloum, Charles Sanders, Sallie Sharpe, Melissa Souza, David A. Williams, Jeanie Woodburn

Edited by Jessie Denning, Rhoda Denning

Illustrations by Don Childers, Jessie Denning, and John C. Dean

ISBN 978-1-62440-096-4

Backwoods Home Magazine
PO Box 712
Gold Beach, OR 97444

Contents

Introduction 6

Poultry breeds

Red Jungle Fowl 8
Buff Orpingtons 11
Put a little color in your flock with Ameraucanas 13
The Dominique: An All-American breed 15
Emden geese for the homestead 18
Add ducks to your flock 21
Raise turkeys and build your own turkey "hooch" 26

Coops & Protection

Home, sweet home 30
Protecting your birds 33
The $50 hen house 37
Controlling airborne predators 41
Keep your chickens safe 44
Use dogs to protect chickens 48
An electric metal barrier to protect your chickens 52
Build a doghouse chicken coop 56
Build a chicken "bunker" 58

Projects

Starting a hen saddle business 64
Build a chicken treat box 66
Simple chicken toys and treats 70
Build an automatic chicken waterer for $20 74

Eggs

Free-range vs. factory-farm eggs 78

Calcium from eggshells 83
What to do with an egg-bound hen 86
Make your eggs last through the winter 88
Long-term egg storage 90

Raising healthy poultry

Raising meat chickens for farmers' markets 94
Prepare your poultry for winter 98
Tips and tricks for the small-scale chicken raiser 102
Raising organic chickens 104
The chicken saga 108
Raise chickens for increased self-reliance 114
    Raise chickens, part two 119
    Raise chickens, part three 126
Feeding the flock 131
Train your chickens (and other livestock) 134
Raising squab for meat 137
Keep your chickens healthy 141
Feeding and watering your chickens 145
Keeping chickens in town 148
Free-range chickens 150

Butchering & Recipes

Butchering chickens made easy 156
Chicken dishes eaten along the Silk Road 160
Make your own charcuterie 167
Squab recipes 171
Duck recipes 174
Canning chicken 180
Quail recipes 184
When turkey takes over the kitchen 188
Cornish hen recipes 194
Chicken dishes from North Africa 196

Introduction

By Piper Emerson-Reed

This book is made up of a collection of articles from the now-retired magazine, *Chickens & Stuff*, which I had the privilege of editing. Previously, this magazine was only available online, but now I have selected the best articles to be bound into this helpful book.

Although some said it was just a fad, there is a continued revival of keeping backyard chickens in America. Kids and adults enjoy taking care of chickens and collecting eggs as a reward for their efforts, and poultry are fun to watch and raise, each with their unique personalities. Some families have even started building coops so beautiful they look like humans should live in them! However, most folks stick to practical coops that are cost-effective, simple to build, and easy to clean. You'll find many different kinds of coops (and instructions how to build them) within the pages of this book.

Some towns now boast veterinary clinics that specialize in dealing with poultry, but for the rural chicken-raiser, this is not an option. Also included in this book are symptoms of common chicken health problems, with cheap, simple, common-sense solutions to bring your chicken back to health.

Whether you are looking for inspiration or are trying to solve a problem with your poultry, this book will be relevant. This book is for all types of chickens — and chicken owners — whether your chickens are backyard pets or homestead livestock. And look for additional information on pigeons, geese, squab, guinea fowl, and turkeys.

POULTRY BREEDS

Red Jungle Fowl

By Sallie Sharpe

Whether you're an urban farmer or have substantial acreage, you are certainly familiar with Rhode Island Reds, Barred Rocks, and many other common large-breed chickens. You can't beat them for eggs and meat. Yet, these birds rely heavily on modern conveniences to survive since most of their natural instincts have been bred out; they can no longer survive on their own or properly raise their young. Another instinct missing is their fear of predators. A Rhode Island Red will just about run up to a coyote and say, "Open wide!" In a world without electricity and stores to purchase feed, it would be very difficult to raise and keep most of the heavy layers, meat birds as well as the dual-purpose chickens.

But don't worry, there happens to be a chicken superhero — a survivor — called the Red Jungle Fowl. Known as the world's feral chicken, this medium-sized bird still runs wild in the forests of India, Burma, and Java, their place of origin. They are even found running free on the islands of Hawaii. They are true survivors.

Red Jungle Fowl just so happens to be the original chicken. All current breeds of chicken have descended from Red Jungle Fowl, just as the modern dog has descended from the wolf. Scientists believe that the Jungle Fowl has been around for eight million years. As people started domesticating the Jungle Fowl, choosing the traits they wanted by selective breeding, the modern chicken emerged. Although most populations of Red Jungle Fowl in the United States and around the world are not one hundred percent purebred, they still retain many of their wild traits.

I was introduced to this superhero among chickens as a child. My granddad acquired a small flock from the zoo in the late 1970s. He allowed his Red Jungle Fowl to run loose, while penning up his large breed chickens. The Red Jungle Fowl not only survived, they thrived on their own. When I inherited the farm, the chickens had been on their own, with limited human interaction, for almost 20 years.

A characteristic which allows the Red Jungle Fowl to survive is their amazing ability to propagate. The hens are smart. They choose inconspicuous places to hide their nests. The color of the Red Jungle Fowl helps the hen to disappear into the forest. She is meekly colored, with brownish feathers with some yellow and orange tint. In about 20 days, the hen will emerge with a huge brood of babies. The chicks are yellowish with wild-looking stripes along their eyes and down their backs.

In a little more than a week, the chicks will be able to fly up and roost high in the trees. This leads to the next astonishing feat of this feral chicken: They can fly quite well. The chicks follow their mom high into the tree line, making them safe from predators. Mom again chooses her spot so that they are well camouflaged within the leaves. She also does a superb job defending her brood. She is so protective, she would probably even fight a lion to save her babies.

The hens are great at raising their young out on their own; however, you will decrease chick mortality by penning them up. It is best to slowly herd them into their pen before the babies get to flying age. Make them a fairly large enclosure, away from too much commotion. Never put more than one hen with babies in the same pen. The females will fight, and they will kill each other's babies in the scuffle.

In warmer climates, such as the south, hens may hatch out all year long. Nearly every year, I am surprised with Christmas chicks. Since the Red Jungle Fowl has such a great success rate with hatching, they can be used to hatch out other types of chickens. If an incubator was no longer an option due to lack of electricity, this would be a convenient way to hatch the larger breeds.

The male Red Jungle Fowl is striking. His colors include many different shades of orange, red, green, and even blue. There is always one dominant rooster. He is easy to spot because he is all pumped up, making him tower over the rest of the flock. Mostly, the roosters coexist without any problems, as long as they are free-range. However, every once in a while,

The chicks are yellowish with wild-looking stripes.

Red Jungle Fowl hens are smart.

The male Red Jungle Fowl is striking.

there will be a battle. One of the younger roosters will put up a challenge. Usually the disagreement is over quickly. Both male and female will forage for food if allowed to roam freely.

The Jungle Fowl, while not having the size of the large-breed chickens, still lay good-sized eggs. If used for meat, the roosters weigh an average of two to three pounds, making them an ample source of protein.

With your large-breed chickens, you get large eggs and more meat. However, without modern conveniences, it would be difficult to sustain these chickens. By adding Red Jungle Fowl to your farm, you get a hardy breed of chicken *and* you get to watch a relic of history do what it does best — thrive.

Buff Orpingtons

By Jackie Clay-Atkinson

One of our favorite homestead chicken breeds is the Buff Orpington. Buff Orpingtons are a versatile breed; they are big enough to be a meat bird, but they also lay plenty of large, brown eggs, even during the winter when some breeds slack off. If you let your Buff hens stay broody, they'll also set on eggs and raise a big brood of baby chicks. We do this with several of our hens every year and that way, we always have plenty of nice fat young cockerels to butcher, come fall — without the hassle of buying baby chicks and brooding them ourselves.

Buff Orpingtons are one color variation of Orpington chickens. Less common are black and lavender (also called blue or slate). The Orpington is named for its country of origin, Orpington, England, where they were bred by William Cook back in 1886. Buffs are one of the "heritage breeds" that have been around for a long time.

Besides their wonderful egg-laying ability, Buff Orpingtons are a beautiful bird. They are a fluffy, shiny gold color that shimmers in the sunlight. And Orpingtons are birds that have sweet dispositions that make them easy to love as a pet. They aren't flighty or nervous as are some other egg-layers. They are active and will rustle out in the yard for their food, keeping an eye out for predators. They can fly, but are so heavy that they prefer not to. You won't find Buff Orpingtons roosting in your trees.

After laying much of the spring, it is not unusual for a hen to suddenly go broody. This means that she is ready to sit on a nest of eggs to hatch her own chicks. She'll puff up her feathers when you reach under her for eggs and she will "growl" at you. Some hens will even peck at your hand, telling you in no uncertain terms that she *wants* those eggs.

A Buff Orpington hen
Photo credit: Pete Cooper

If you've had a rooster in the coop so the eggs are fertile, you can let her accumulate a clutch and begin setting. But it's a good idea to take the hen and her eggs into a private location where other hens won't try to lay more eggs in the same nest box. If you don't move her, her own eggs will get broken and you'll have a mish-mash of different-age eggs, very few of which will hatch. I like to put mama hen and her eggs into a small dog crate, bedded well with hay, and keep her in the barn where she won't be disturbed. It's easy to keep her in feed and water, happily waiting until her eggs hatch into little yellow, fluffy chicks.

As Buff Orpingtons are so quiet and docile, they make a perfect bird for urban homesteaders. Buff Orpingtions are quite happy in a small coop and run or in a smaller chicken tractor. Barring crowing roosters, the only sound they'll make is a contented quiet clucking or a bit louder cackle when they brag about the big egg they just laid.

Many children have Buff Orpington hens for pets. The hens look forward to free-ranging time with "their" children on the lawn or in the garden. My youngest son, David, had a Buff Orpington chick he was given because its leg was stiff on hatching. He gave it careful range of motion exercises several times a day and plenty of love and care. It lived in a box in his bedroom. Soon it was hopping around normally. They were inseparable and Buffy went everywhere David did — on his bike, hiking, and even snowmobiling! It was a big day when Buffy laid her first brown egg.

It is common for Buff Orpingtons to weigh eight to ten pounds or more at maturity. While Orpingtons take longer to reach butchering size than do the super meat birds, Cornish Crosses, they don't suffer the health issues such as heart and leg problems like the meat birds do. The Buff Orpingtons dress out nicely with a pretty yellow cast to their skin making them quite attractive as roasting chickens.

The egg-laying ability of Buff Orpingtons is well known. It is not uncommon for a Buff hen to lay 175 to 200 nice, big, light-brown eggs a year. And because they are well feathered and are a large breed, they aren't affected much by the cold, laying right through the winter months. (It does help to hang a light in the coop at night so they aren't affected by shortening daylight hours in the winter.) They are not a "fussy" breed. Buffs are hardy, and if taken care of properly, they are not prone to illnesses or parasites.

Buff Orpingtons are easy for children to handle.

Buff Orpingtons are a nice breed to show in 4-H because they are beautiful, docile, and easy for children to handle. All of my children have had a chicken project and we were very excited when they brought home blue ribbons and grand champion awards with their beautiful, well-cared-for Buff Orpingtons. We also used to show our chickens in the open classes at the county fair and our shining Orpingtons were always a stand-out. The whole family had lots of fun exhibiting at the fair.

Luckily, Buff Orpingtons are a very common breed so it isn't terribly hard for you to find chicks or young adult birds to buy. Several mail-order hatcheries carry them, as do many local farm stores and feed mills in the spring.

Some hatcheries that we have dealt with are:

Murray McMurray Hatchery
PO Box 458
Webster City, IA 50595
Phone: 800-456-3280
www.mcmurrayhatchery.com

Cackle Hatchery
PO Box 529
Lebanon, MO 65536
417-532-4581
www.cacklehatchery.com

Welp Hatchery
PO Box 77
Bancroft, IA 50517
800-458-4473
www.welphatchery.com

All of the above have free catalogs or you can browse and order from their websites.

I hope you'll consider Buff Orpingtons as an addition to your own homestead. We sure love ours! Right now our Buffs are scratching out under the fruit trees in our little orchard, singing cheerfully.

Put a little color in your flock with Ameraucanas

By Jackie Clay-Atkinson

The colors in our egg basket really pop when I gather eggs because in among the brown and white eggs are blue, green, and khaki-colored eggs. Our grandchildren, Mason and Ava, love to gather eggs on our homestead. Grandma and Grandpa's chickens lay Easter eggs — no coloring required.

We enjoy having at least a few Ameraucanas on the homestead. Not only do they lay beautifully-colored eggs, but these chickens look unusual too. Some have beards and puffs of ear muff feathers.

Ameraucanas are derived from the unusual South American Araucana. The Araucana comes from Chile and is a "rumpless" fowl, with no tailbone or tail feathers. Araucanas, like Ameraucanas, also have ear tufts. Unfortunately, ear tufts create a genetically lethal combination when a tufted rooster is bred to a tufted hen; a high percentage of the chicks die in the eggs. When Araucanas became popular in the United States, many breeders began crossing the Araucanas with other breeds in order to keep the blue egg-laying trait but have a higher chick survival rate. The result became a new pure breed called Ameraucana, although they have beards and tail feathers.

But by whatever name or breeding, I love my Ameraucanas! They are usually a brown-

To the right are two of our Ameraucana hens — one a grizzled gray, the other a mix of brown and black penciling.

Ameraucanas lay lots of large blue or bluish-tinted eggs. Beards and tail feathers distinguish Ameracaunas from Araucanas.

ish, black-barred, or other muted color, which hides them from hawks and other predators. Ameraucanas are quite friendly and pleasant to be around in the coop. They are very seldom flighty and cluck around your feet like pets begging for treats. My kids have always had Ameraucanas as pets, sometimes even training them to walk on a leash. They are also a dual-purpose breed — good for both meat and eggs. They are a breed with small pea comb and plenty of feathering, so they are quite winter hardy. Even when other breeds stop laying, the Ameraucanas still pop out those brightly-colored eggs. Ameraucanas are very motherly and will go broody if allowed to sit on a clutch of eggs. I even had one hen fly in the face of a fox to save her chicks from danger. That fox retreated with his tail held low!

Be careful when you buy Ameraucana chicks or adult birds. The red flag with some sellers is the spelling of the word "Ameraucana." If it's spelled "Americana," it means that the birds are not purebred, and that their eggs may not be blue-colored. It is pretty easy to find purebred Ameraucana chickens as many breeders keep them because they are so popular. We have purchased Ameraucanas from a few favorite mail order hatcheries such as Murray McMurray Hatchery (www.mcmurrayhatchery.com) and Fowl Stuff (www.fowlstuff.com).

The chicks are delivered to the post office, housed in a flat cardboard box with air holes in the sides. There is usually a minimum order requirement so that the day-old chicks will stay warm enough to survive during shipment cross-country.

If you're interested in serious breeding or showing at poultry shows or fairs, please buy your Ameraucanas from a reputable breeder so you get show stock. You can contact the Ameraucana Breeders Club (www.Ameraucana.org). Another helpful website for serious breeders is www.poultryshowcentral.com.

If you are looking for something a little bit different to add to your chicken coop, why not consider some Ameraucanas? You'll love their appearance, their personalities, and most of all, those beautiful blue-shaded eggs!

The Dominique

An All-American breed

By Charles Sanders

If you are looking for a unique and truly All-American breed of chicken, then the Dominique will fit the bill. This rare breed of chicken is entirely American and was developed in early colonial America. There, settlers had brought chickens of different varieties over from the Old Country. The Dominique breed came about from random and rampant crossbreeding of those original birds and by farmers who recognized superior traits of several different breeds, probably those brought over from southern England. Records also indicate that there might be a Caribbean influence in the bloodline as well. Basically, though, they are the "mutts" of the poultry world.

History

Dominiques were popular during the 1700s, and by the mid-1800s they had become the most popular breed of chicken in the country. Over the years, American settlers took these birds with them as they pushed westward into the frontier. Soon, the breed was spread over America all the way to the Pacific.

Dominiques had to be tough to survive homestead life in colonial and early America. During that time, chickens were definitely not treated as pets, and were left largely to forage and fend for themselves. They roosted at night in trees or at best, on a pole in the barn. As a result, the Dominique developed into a hardy bird that could pretty well feed itself.

This breed also survived through the 1920s and '30s, the time of the Great Depression. Their hardiness served them well during those lean times. My folks called these big birds Dominickers and liked their large size, hardy habits, and big brown eggs. On those Depression-era scratch farms, the old Dominickers again proved themselves in scratching out a living on meager fare. For those poor families, they

Dominique chickens are truly an American breed. This drawing from 1882 shows a Dominique rooster and hen, looking exactly as the breed does today. The rooster displays the rose-type comb, characteristic of the breed.

A Dominique hen (Photo courtesy of Ron Proctor)

provided meat for the pot, eggs for the skillet, and chicks to replenish the flock.

With the development and importation of other heavy, fancy breeds of chickens, the chicken breed that actually helped to settle the country sadly fell by the wayside. In fact, by the 1950s, it was thought the breed might be extinct.

By the end of World War II, commercial poultry operations and large chicken farms were beginning to pop up and smaller homestead flocks were beginning to dwindle in number. As a result, the Dominique began to wane in popularity. By 1970, there were only four flocks of Dominiques known to exist. The American Livestock Breeds Conservancy (ALBC) is America's leading nonprofit organization working to protect livestock and poultry breeds from extinction. They noted that from 1983 to 2006, Dominiques increased in numbers throughout the country. After another decline beginning in about 2007, the breed is seeing another surge in popularity as folks become more interested in self-sufficiency and in rare and heritage breeds. They are currently on the ALBC's "Watch List" of rare breeds. What that means is that there are fewer than 5,000 breeding birds in the United States.

Attributes

Dominiques are fairly large birds, weighing in at about 7 or 8 pounds. They have rose combs and resemble a souped-up version of the Barred Rock in appearance. That rose-type comb helps to identify them from the Barred Rock, which has a larger single comb, but similar black-and-white barred plumage. A rose comb sits tighter on the bird's head and helps keep it from being frostbitten. The barring on their feathering is also more broken up than that of the more uniformly barred feathers of the Barred Rock. That plumage tends to be tight and historically helped to keep the birds warm in their harsh environments. That was another trait that made them popular as low-maintenance birds. In addition, that plentiful plumage made them popular among the farm wives for stuffing pillows. It's also been recorded that the barred plumage helped to hide the foraging birds from predators. For the pioneer children sent to gather the eggs, it often meant keeping an eye on the hens to see just where they hid their nests.

Like some other types of homestead livestock, they are a dual-purpose breed and are popular for both their meat and large brown eggs. They mature early and can start laying at about six months of age.

The modern Dominique raiser

If you select this breed for your own homestead flock, you will not be disappointed. In fact, today, the Dominique is seeing a bit of a surge in popularity. This is due in part to the heightened awareness of folks regarding clean, wholesome food. Another factor is the large number of people who are simply striving to become more self-reliant. Finally, a number of aficionados of this old breed, and rare breeds in general, are choosing it to help keep the species alive.

No special care is needed for their chicks. If you are purchasing them from a hatchery, either local or mail order, simply follow the directions provided, or treat them as you would other chicks.

Once they reach adulthood, Dominiques do best if allowed to forage about on the homestead; however, they will also do well in a coop or chicken yard. They begin laying as early as six months of age and will lay up to around 270 eggs per year. Their nice size also makes them good candidates for the frying pan.

Dominique hens are excellent brooders, a trait that helped make them popular on early homesteads and farms. They are also quiet and good-tempered, making them suitable for a family flock. However, the roosters of the breed can tend to be on the aggressive side and have even been known to kill small predators such as cats, snakes, and mink. So, choose your birds accordingly. As the chicks mature, the roosters might be the first ones to consider for the frying pan or freezer.

A true heritage breed, the Dominique deserves consideration on every homestead as an "All-American Fowl."

Resources

Dominique chicks are available from a few hatcheries. Try contacting one of these hatcheries for your chicks or viable eggs:

- Murray McMurray Hatchery (www.mcmurrayhatchery.com)
- Nantahala Farm (www.nantahala-farm.com)
- Cackle Hatchery (www.cacklehatchery.com)

Emden geese for the homestead

By Samantha Biggers

For those looking for a good homestead goose for meat, eggs, and fertilizer, the Emden might just be the goose for the job. Originally from Germany, not only are they very hardy, but they are also the largest breed of goose in the world. They make a visually impressive addition to your farm. Farms report weights that vary quite a bit, but you can count on your Emdens to weigh between 16-25 pounds when mature. Sometimes males are smaller than females and sometimes they are a lot larger. Don't make the mistake of using size to determine the sex of your birds.

Although the Emden is raised commercially, it is a very old breed that came to the United States as early as 1820. I mention this because many commercial poultry breeds are not known for their vigor and foraging ability.

Geese will rely heavily on clover and grass for their diet. In a world where feed prices are consistently rising, any animal that can live and thrive on mostly grass makes a lot of sense for farms of all sizes. In the past, we have raised heavy Cornish Cross broiler chickens. Although they do grow fast, they require large amounts of high protein feed and are not as hearty as geese. If the grass is growing, our geese will walk away from grain feed and eat the grass instead. When they do want a little grain feed they find us and honk at us. They will continue to forage as much as they can through the winter but you will have to increase the amount of grain you give them as forage gets more scarce. This will vary depending on the climate where you live and how hard the winter months are.

Most geese are very cold-tolerant and the Emden is no exception. Ours can be seen taking baths in their stock tank or pond when it

is 5° F outside. This makes them a great choice for meat and egg production in colder climates, where raising chicks can be a lot more challenging without a heat source.

Stocking rates for larger geese should be no more than 25 per acre if you intend on them getting most of their food from the land. It is important to remember that a goose needs to forage greens in order to be healthy. If you ever isolate a goose due to injury or other reasons, make sure to regularly pick them some greens.

While a three-gallon bucket of water changed daily can be enough for a trio of geese, they prefer to have enough water so they are able to take a nice bath. A 40-gallon stock tank will be good for a trio of geese to bathe in, but having a tub or pond of that size or larger also helps encourage and ensure the successful mating of geese. On the other hand, they can do just fine with a few buckets of water set out for them so long as you make sure to change them daily.

Geese are useful for the fertilizer they provide as well. Geese are large birds and the amount of manure they add to your topsoil is pretty significant. This can be very useful for the home gardener or fruit grower.

Goose behavior

Fixations

Geese can be very obsessive about shiny objects. I made the mistake of leaving some aluminum cans where they could get to them. I had to go outside that night and pick up the cans again in order to recycle them because the geese "dabbled" at them so much the noise woke us up and they had scattered the cans everywhere. This can get them in trouble sometimes. We had a scare when one of our female geese ate a long string with a nail at the end of it. Although we just cut the end off after removing what string we could, it definitely gave us a scare because we were not sure if the string would cause any internal problems.

The myth of the mean goose

Sure, geese can be ill-tempered like any other animal, but they really don't deserve the bad reputation they get for temperament. Just because a goose puts its neck down low and comes towards you while it is honking does not mean that it is trying to attack. This is goose language for "Hey, what's going on?" or "You got any food?" Geese are very social creatures and will become quite attached to you if you pay them attention or raise them from a gosling. If you talk to them, they will be louder generally.

Just because a goose puts its neck down low and comes towards you does not mean that it is trying to attack.

At the same time, you have to be careful with geese when they are nesting and feeling protective. Male geese seem to be a bit more ill-tempered than the females. Our main male goose will hiss a bit and lower his head, even run at you, but he has never bothered anyone. Even good geese might attack a dog or other small animal if there is any suspicion that the geese are under threat. Small children can be troublesome with geese because they can be a little too enthusiastic. Children are sometimes the same height as an Emden, so the child is naturally more vulnerable than an adult.

Temperament can vary depending upon the breed of goose you choose to raise. Emden geese are intimidating to many because of their large size but do not have as bad a reputation as some breeds such as the Egyptian.

Geese and predators

Over the years, we have lost quite a few chickens to small varmints. We have only lost one goose — it was young and not an Emden. Once an Emden goose is grown, they make a very formidable opponent for predators. Not many small varmints want to take on a

20-pound bird with a four-foot wingspan. It is really nice not to have to worry about them so much when they are out foraging. Dogs quickly learn what a goose can do with its bill. Geese are also very good at honking loudly to let you know that varmints are around.

Eggs

There are varying claims as to how many eggs an Emden will lay per year. I have heard figures anywhere from 20-60 eggs. I would say somewhere in the middle is a good estimate. One reason it can be hard to determine is that they like to hide their eggs, so it is easy for a flock owner to miss a few here and there.

Some flock owners make money by selling eggs to others for incubating. Goose eggs need to be incubated within seven days of laying for best hatch results. This can be a challenge since geese hide their eggs if they have a chance, and as a result, you can't be sure how long ago the egg was laid.

If you choose to eat Emden eggs, remember that one of their eggs is as large as four large chicken eggs. Goose and duck eggs are best used for baking, although I have heard that cracking and cooking the eggs in water will reduce some of the "rubbery" texture that some use to describe them when fried like a chicken egg.

A goose nest is much larger than a chicken nest.

Reproduction

Geese make big and elaborate nests on the ground. One has to keep in mind that geese don't just lay their eggs any old place like a chicken can. Often they will cover their eggs up, especially if they are starting to feel like building a real nest and setting. Generally, you can expect them to set for at least 28 days, but this can vary a few days in either direction. If a goose has not come off its nest by the 40 day mark, you should consider breaking up the nest so she is not just wasting her time.

Goslings

Goslings command a good price in the spring. Ordering goslings costs about $15 each when shipping is accounted for. You may get a better bargain by ordering a greater quantity. If you have extra goose eggs, you might consider incubating them and selling the goslings or raising them for your own flock to save money.

Goslings should be given a good gamebird starter feed when young. The more you let them eat, the faster they will grow. It is amazing to watch how fast a goose grows. Within four weeks, you will have a Emden goose the size of a broiler chicken. Remember that your goslings will eat less feed as they get older and become better at foraging.

Selling butchered geese

In some areas there may be a demand around the holiday season for dressed birds. Some states allow you to butcher and sell them from your home. Make sure to check your local laws before marketing your meat. The holiday goose market can be quite lucrative when one considers that a goose at the grocery store costs at least $50. Part of this high price is due to volume. People don't eat as many geese as chicken, for example. Another aspect is that geese have to be raised on green forage and not a lot of cheap commodity corn.

Add ducks to your flock

By Samantha Biggers

Ducks are a lively and useful addition to many homesteads. Unlike chickens, ducks need a decent amount of water in order to be happy and healthy. If you don't have a pond, don't worry. There are many ways to address the water issue when raising ducks.

Breeds of ducks

There are too many breeds to highlight in one article, but here is a general overview of your basic duck types. Thoroughly research any breed you are considering to ensure that you are getting the duck that is right for you.

Ornamental ducks

There are countless breeds of beautiful ducks out there. One of the more popular varieties is the Chinese Wood Duck. They are known for their unique colors. Though small, they add a lot of character to your wetlands and are great if you like to watch beautiful birds. I include the Mallard breed as an ornamental because they are too small for meat production and lay too few eggs. There is a chance that your Mallards will fly away. Expect to pay $50-$100 per duck for Wood Ducks or some of the rare and hard-to-raise ornamentals.

Meat ducks

Your typical meat duck is a breed known as the Peking. They are a large white duck and although they are a commercial duck, they are excellent foragers of slugs, insects, worms, green forage, etc. If you are really serious about meat production or marketing meat ducks, then this is the breed for you.

Rouen

The Rouen looks a lot like a large, dark Mallard. The standard white Peking duck stands out to predators with its bright feathering, but the dark-colored Rouen easily hides. They are considerably smaller than a Peking,

which is the standard meat duck. The Rouen is an old and established breed that is easy to find from virtually any commercial factory or even chain feed stores.

Muscovy ducks

Muscovy ducks are large ducks. While males can weigh 15 pounds, a female might weigh 8 pounds. They can be used for meat or eggs. Their heart and livers are used to make homeopathic flu remedies, such as Oscillococcinum. Muscovy ducks will roost in trees like chickens if given the opportunity.

Feeding ducks

There are many different options for feeding ducks. Some antibiotics in medicated feed are toxic to ducks, so make sure to read the label on the feed before you buy it. Chick starters that are medicated should never be used for ducks. Most ducks like to forage, so I don't recommend them for someone that does not have a yard that can some space set aside for this. Ducks are much happier when they have room to forage, plus it helps save on your feed

Ducks are entertaining to watch. To the left, Momma duck teaches these juvenile ducks how to forage. Below, ducks take an afternoon bath in the pond.

bill. But ducks need some animal protein to survive. You cannot have a healthy vegetarian duck. If they are in confinement at all, you have to make sure they have feed that has animal protein in it — not just soy and corn. One creative method for adding protein to your duck's diet is to have a light that attracts bugs to their area. They will gobble them up and it can be fun to watch. I have heard of people even using a bug zapper for this. Adolescent and adult ducks can be fed a game bird maintenance ration. The amount they eat will depend on how much forage they have. Most ducks that are used to people will let you know if they are hungry by getting close to you and making a lot of "whacking" or "honking" sounds.

A galvanized feed pan of water makes for safe duckling swimming lessons.

Duckling feed

A good start is essential when raising ducks, so buy the best feed you can. Game bird starter of 20% protein or better is recommended for all ducklings. You can get away with starting ducklings with a 16% protein feed, but they do much better on a higher protein feed at first and the price difference per bag is small. Do not feed medicated feed to ducklings unless it is labeled specifically for ducks, as it can be toxic to them.

Water and ducklings

If the ducklings have their mother, she will oil them and they will be able to swim and not sink. If you have ducklings that you are raising without their mother, you will need to provide them with a feed pan of water so they can dunk their heads and not get the condition known as "sticky eye." A galvanized feed pan that is a few inches deep and changed a few times a day will do with a few ducklings. It is best to also place some stones or pieces of wood in the pan so they can hop in and out. Since they don't have a mother duck to oil them, they are at a greater risk for drowning in deep water until they start to feather out more.

Dealing with sticky eye

If a baby duck cannot open its eye, there is a good chance it has sticky eye. This condition is caused when the duckling does not get its eye flushed out properly. The sooner it is treated, the easier it is to cure. If this happens on our farm, we use saline solution to rinse the eyes and a clean cotton swab to very gently clean any drainage or residue from the eye. This needs to happen several times the first day. If the condition does not improve some within 24 hours, you can continue to rinse and clean but then apply some eye ointment containing Terramycin with a cotton swab. If this is done for a few days the duckling usually recovers. Improvements can often be seen much quicker. Make sure that the duckling is able to eat during treatment. You might have to help them eat in some cases.

Parasite control with ducks

Ducks are useful in preventing harmful parasites on a farm. These pests include the following:

Ticks

These critters can cause a condition called Lyme Disease and are notorious for hiding in the clothes of those who have been outdoors.

Liver flukes

This nasty fluke can infect the lungs of mammals such as cattle and goats on your farm. Ducks have been shown to be extremely effective in preventing this malady entirely by eating the snails that host this parasite.

General worms

There are all kinds of worms that can appear on a farm. Ducks like to eat all of them.

In order to utilize ducks more effectively on your farm, rotate them throughout your farm in a pattern that works best for you. There might be a certain time of year where your garden has been harvested but there is still green cover. That might mean it is a good time to let the ducks graze and rid your garden of pests as well as fertilize your next crop. An added benefit is that the ducks will help eat down the last bits of your previous garden which makes your job easier when you cultivate it again.

Momma duck sits on hatching eggs.

Older now, the ducklings are curious about their surroundings.

Reproduction

Ducks start breeding in early spring. Exact dates are going to vary based on your location. Ducks in the south will start to think about breeding a lot sooner than those in the northern regions. Ducks can be loud and flashy during breeding season. Males often fight each other regularly during this time. It is not always the largest duck that wins either. We had a mixed flock of Saxony and Mallard ducks — the male Mallard was less than half the size of the male Saxony, but he succeeded in fathering the vast majority of the ducklings hatched that season. I have never had a male duck become aggressive towards people during mating season, unlike some other birds such as geese.

A duck will build a nest and clutch of as many as two dozen eggs with less than 10 being the most common. Duck setting times vary from 28-35 days. On our farm we had one duck hatch 15 ducklings; she seemed a bit frazzled having to watch out for that many ducks. She really tried hard to fit all of them under her when they wanted to hide or get warm but she couldn't quite manage to cover all of them.

Some breeds of duck are more likely to set and hatch a clutch of eggs naturally without much intervention on your part. That does not mean that you should not be open to breeds that do not set well.

If you like a breed that does not go broody very easily, you always have the option of using an inexpensive incubator and hatching out some ducklings yourself. For less than $150, you can get an incubator and egg turner that will allow you to hatch around 40 eggs. This can also be a way to earn some extra money from your flock. With the most common breeds of ducklings selling for at least $5 each, this can add up. Especially when you consider that many people will pay more for ducklings from a local breeder than from a chain feed store. Ornamental ducks can fetch a very high price per duckling.

Keeping ducks safe

Although ducks can see better at night than chickens, they are slow movers and are vulnerable to flying night predators such as large owls. You might be thinking that a big meat duck is too large for such a bird, but if you live where there are Great Horned Owls, you are wrong. Ducks are the most vulnerable when they are really young. Short of total confinement at night, there are some things you can do in order to protect your ducks.

Shelter and cover

Ducks are semi-nocturnal and have some night vision. This is also important to remember if you ever have to catch a duck. The bottom line is: they like to party at night. When

Ornamental ducklings can fetch a high price.

you first start raising ducks, it can make you think there is something bothering your ducks. Usually, what is going on is just chattering, swimming, mating, and feasting on bugs and worms.

Ducks are pretty good at taking cover. If they have something to get under, they can avoid some attacks. It doesn't have to be fancy. Some people use netting to form a canopy over an area for their ducks to gather, but that can be expensive and a bit of a hassle.

Flashing lights

Many farmers have successfully used a wide array of flashing or bright lights to help deter predators. It works very well for deterring owls away from your flock. Cheap holiday lights will work if they are at least outdoor grade. The lights work by messing with the night vision of nocturnal predators.

Enjoying ducks

I have to say that ducks are funny and engaging creatures. They will approach you and chatter away so long as they have been treated with a kind hand in the past. If they have been swatted at a lot by a previous owner then it might take a bit of time to win them over but that can usually be done with a bit of grain feed and just sitting still with them for a while.

Ducks are pretty amusing to watch. Especially when they get into a pond or teach young ducks how to dive and dabble.

Raise turkeys

and build your own "turkey hooch"

By Jackie Clay-Atkinson

Most homesteads include chickens, but a lot of folks think having turkeys is hard and somewhat mysterious. Turkeys have an undeserved reputation as being hard to raise, so few people actually try. In fact, turkeys are quite easy to raise on a homestead, requiring basically the same care and feed as do chickens.

One caution, however: Don't try to breed adult commercial breeds such as the Broad Breasted Bronze, Broad Breasted White, or Giant White. This is where the reputation for being "hard to raise" comes in. These breeds are like commercial Cornish Rock meat chickens. They have been bred to produce lots of meat quickly ... not to reproduce naturally. They are too heavy to enjoy a long life and when an adult tom jumps on the back of an adult hen turkey, he will claw her back severely while trying to stay in place to mate. This often kills the hens. In the old days, farmers would buy or make turkey "saddles" out of canvas to tie on the backs of hen turkeys so the males would not claw their backs during mating. But today, turkeys have been bred to be even heavier and require artificial insemination to breed.

So what do homesteaders do? Well, if you just want to raise a couple of meat turkeys for holiday meals, go ahead and buy these commercial breeds. They will make lots of tasty meat quickly under good homestead conditions and care. Buy and raise them right along with your spring chicks. But, if you'd like to raise a few turkeys each year, your best route is to raise old-fashioned heritage breed turkeys.

By raising heritage breeds, such as these Bourbon Red and Narragansett toms, we can naturally breed turkeys with plenty of meat.

There are many breeds that have been around a long time for the simple reason that they can naturally reproduce. These heritage breeds are not as heavy as the modern meat breeds, so they can mate and the hens will sit on their own eggs to hatch them.

Choose a breed that you like the looks of, from the smoky gray Slates to the gorgeous mahogany and white Bourbon Reds. We picked Bourbon Reds and Narragansett as they are large heritage breeds. Each year, our hens lay plenty of eggs and sit on a nest or two, raising their own poults with no help from us.

Free-range or confinement

While we all like the idea of letting our poultry range wherever they wish, it is a little dangerous for the birds. Back when we lived at our farm in Sturgeon Lake, Minnesota, we had several free-ranging hen turkeys. Our farm was surrounded by fields and woods. In the spring, we'd suddenly miss a hen and worry that a wolf or coyote had picked her for dinner. Then in about three weeks, down the road she'd come with a dozen or so poults following her. She'd gone off into the woods to hide her nest, lay her eggs, and brood them successfully.

We've had a couple escapees do just that here on our current homestead. But this can be dangerous as we have had coyotes pick off nesting birds. So, instead, we've resorted to penning our birds in during breeding season then turning the moms and poults into our one-acre orchard to "free range" the rest of the year.

Building and using turkey hooches

Each hen and tom, or a couple hens the same breed as the tom, are penned in one of our winter goat barn pens with outside corrals. And inside is a special nest box my husband, Will, made one cold winter day, right in our living room. We call them "turkey hooches" for the barracks back in the Vietnam War, constructed with assorted scrap and corrugated galvanized steel panels.

As turkeys are quite large and very secretive about their nests, an open box doesn't attract them. And if two or more hen turkeys lay eggs in the same open nest, they usually break their eggs while trying to take over the entire nest for themselves. We went an entire year without raising *any* poults before the hooches were built.

So what the heck is a turkey hooch? It's basically a box framed with 2x2-inch lumber, boxed in on all four sides with a floor with scrap plywood or OSB. The roof is simply a square of corrugated steel roofing bent over a 2x2-inch ridge "pole." The dimensions of our hooches are 18x18x24 inches. The peak of the roof is 24 inches above the floor. These dimensions let our turkeys stand up, turn around, and settle down to brood their eggs in comfort.

Will screwed the hooch together with 1- and 2½-inch deck screws for ease of construction, as nailing the two-inch frame might have split the lightweight lumber. The 1-inch screws fastened the plywood and OSB to the frame and the longer screws fastened the framework together.

The front piece has a curved shape to fit underneath the curved metal roof and a door cut in it large enough for the turkey to enter easily. Some turkeys are quite shy about their nest and you can, if you wish, staple a piece of fabric, such as an old towel, over the door for even more seclusion. I would do this after the hen has started using the nest so she'll get the idea before the door is further enclosed.

A coat of paint will keep our finished turkey hooches nice for years to come.

We had scrap pieces of corrugated metal roofing that had been given to us by a friend who thought Will could find a use for them. But you can cut any metal roofing scraps to size using a circular saw with the blade inserted backwards. Whether cutting metal or wood, please use gloves and safety glasses.

By pre-drilling holes in the roof, Will easily screwed the roofing in place with deck screws, fastening it to the 2x2-inch framework on the sides and top. For bedding in the hooches, we use about two inches of wood shavings and dry straw on top of that so the hen can hollow out a nice soft nesting spot. We've found that our turkey hens really love our hooches!

If two turkey hens use the same hooch, it's a good idea to move one of them to another pen with her hooch so she won't crowd the other hen. As I've said, two or more turkeys trying to sit on the same nest results in many or all of the eggs getting broken. This is why we don't let our turkeys set eggs in the orchard poultry yard. Chickens also start laying eggs in the turkey's nest and even after she starts to brood her eggs, the chickens still lay in her nest. Soon turkey-chicken conflicts break eggs and it's all downhill from there.

Turkeys start laying quite early in the spring, often before nighttime temperatures are above freezing, so the eggs will freeze. If this happens we gather the eggs as soon as they're laid, holding them in egg cartons on the counter, and we replace them with chicken eggs. Yep, the chicken eggs will freeze; we just replace them the next day. Turkeys can't tell the difference and the eggs will keep the hen laying in the hooch. We gather a nice batch of turkey eggs then hatch them in our little foam incubator. Heritage turkey poults generally sell for about $10 each or more so it can provide enough "turkey income" to buy feed for the flock.

Once nighttime temperatures have warmed up, we let her go ahead and set a clutch of eggs.

Once the hen starts to brood her eggs, it will take about 28 days before they start to hatch. She will turn them as needed; no interference on your part is needed. Once the poults hatch, the hen will leave the nest with them. The poults can eat the same 18% protein poultry food as the parents. Make sure there is a shallow water pan in the pen with the poults (not too deep, or they will drown).

Poults of heritage breeds take longer to reach maturity and butchering size than do modern commercial breeds. If you're planning on Thanksgiving turkey, you'll need to harvest 1½-year-old birds, as those hatched in the spring will be too small to eat if you're used to a 20-pound holiday bird. Given good care, these "older" birds won't be tough.

We range our turkeys with our chickens, but a lot of expert advice says that turkeys will pass blackhead, a turkey disease, on to the chickens. This may be true in commercial conditions where thousands of birds are housed together. But I was a veterinary technician for more than 20 years and have homesteaded with both turkeys and chickens for more than 40 years and have never seen a single bird with blackhead.

If you've ever thought you might like to add turkeys to your homestead flock, please do. They're fun, beautiful, and easy to raise. Especially if you use Will's idea for their hooches. Pick a heritage breed you love and help save it from extinction. One of our breeds, the Narragansetts, at one time had a dozen or fewer breeding turkeys in this country. Now, thanks mainly to hobby breeders and homesteaders, the numbers are much larger.

COOPS & PROTECTION

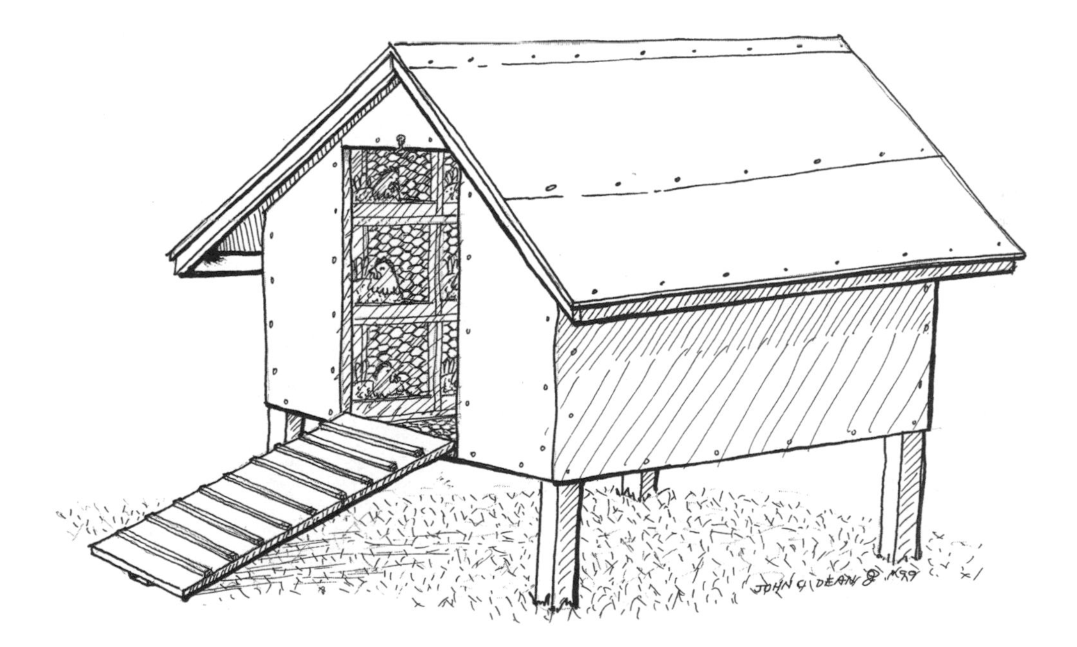

Home, sweet home

Chicken coops come in many styles

By Charles Sanders

If there is one thing about chicken raisers, we're an inventive lot. The growing popularity of raising one's own chickens is also resulting in a wide variety of styles and materials used in the construction of the ol' chicken house. Some of us are minimalists and give our birds a simple shed to call home. Others like to go all out and provide some pretty fancy digs for their birds.

Chickens don't really require much in the way of housing, but with more and more people looking at their birds as pets rather than livestock, some pretty nice facilities have popped up. In reality, as long as you have a shelter that is dry, with a place to lay eggs, and have food and water available, you'll do alright.

A henhouse should be ventilated, but not drafty. It should not be built too tight, either. There should be some airflow in the building. Chickens give off quite a bit of moisture and if cooped up in too tight a space, they can develop respiratory problems.

Figure 1: Our old chicken house and pen

Some poultry raisers like for their birds to be on a solid floor, others on bare dirt. Still others build their chicken houses so that the birds can run in an area with a wire bottom that allows

Figure 2: An attractive and functional henhouse and run for a family living in a development

Figure 3: The designer of this henhouse included a door to access the hen nests. It is even equipped with a hydraulic assist!

Figure 4: Another elevated pen that allows the droppings to fall to the ground beneath the run

droppings and waste grain to fall to the ground beneath. Any of these methods are suitable. The secret is to keep dry bedding and scratch material in the coop and run. You don't want your birds having to slog around in constantly wet and soiled bedding.

Out in the sticks, you can build just about any structure you wish. Our old chicken house was actually one half of a building I built (Figure 1). The chickens' quarters occupied the west half of the building. The easternmost half was a combination toolshed and storeroom for chicken feed, grit, and other poultry supplies like lights, extra feeders, and so forth. The chicken run was on the south side of the building and had a small door that allowed the birds to come and go. The sliding door was actually controlled from inside the toolshed half of the building and was raised and lowered by using a line and small pulley. I could raise and lower it without having to go into the chicken house itself.

Figure 5: This coop has an open pen built beneath the house itself.

In Figures 2 and 3, you can see a well-made and attractive little hen house. This one was built in a housing development. Due to some restrictions there, the poultry raiser had to get rid of his rooster. It turns out that the rooster was a bit too disruptive in sounding his morning wake-up calls and some of the other residents objected to what they felt was excessive noise! This poultry raiser was able to keep the hens and house them in this area of his backyard. They get to range occasionally, but for most part, he is a guerilla poultry farmer.

Figure 4 demonstrates another elevated pen that allows the droppings to fall to the ground below. Keeping the coop clean is a priority for owners who want healthy chickens.

In Figure 5, you can see a style of chicken house that is made by some folks here locally. It has an open pen directly beneath the henhouse itself for all the birds to scratch and forage. The birds move to and from that grazing area through a small opening in the floor of the henhouse. The walk-in door is on the other end of the coop. On this end, you might also see the axles that can accommodate wheels to make the house mobile. That enables the structures to be moved to fresh pickings for the birds.

Whatever you decide, wherever you live, use your imagination as you design your chicken house. It may end up being a traditional poultry house; it might be a neatly-designed and painted one to blend in with your urban environment. Use what you have, wherever you are, and adapt it to your needs. The end goal remains the same: to raise clean, healthy, and wholesome meat and eggs from your own chicken flock.

Protecting your birds

By Allen Easterly

Whether you raise chickens, quail, doves, or other birds outdoors, there is always some hungry predator looking for an easy meal. Here on my farm, we raise meat chickens, egg-laying chickens, doves, squab (meat pigeons), two breeds of quail, and someday we may branch out to pheasant. We are located on the border of a million acres of U.S. Forest Service land, so we have plenty of predators right at our back door, including bears, bobcats, coyotes, red and gray foxes, raccoons, opossums, skunks, hawks, owls, eagles, and others. Each breed of bird has its own housing requirements and certain predators that seek it out for a tasty snack. Our job is to protect our fine feathered friends. Sometimes solutions are expensive, requiring large, strong coops, and other times it's very simple and inexpensive. Through lots of trial and error, I finally came up with solutions to protect my birds from just about any wild critter.

Meat chickens

Chickens raised for meat are short-lived and only need temporary protection, so no large coops or expensive solutions are really necessary for a small flock owner. For the first four weeks of a meat bird's life it must be kept at warm temperatures under brooder lamps until it grows enough feathers to keep itself warm. To maintain the heat, this usually has to be done inside a barn or outbuilding. The best way to protect chicks at this stage is to use a completely enclosed building; that way there really aren't any predatory threats to the birds.

Once the birds are past four weeks of age, they can either remain in the enclosed building until butchering day or they can be put outdoors in a chicken tractor. I have build a couple 10x10x2-foot simple do-it-yourself chicken tractors from PVC pipe and chicken wire. I covered part of the roof and one corner with plastic roofing panels. The panels give protection from the weather and the birds tend to spend the night in the covered corner. That corner protection prevents raccoons from reaching through the wire. You'll know if a raccoon is a problem when you start finding birds with only their heads missing. The chicken wire on the remaining roof prevents successful attacks by hawks. They still attack but get a big surprise when they hit that wire. It doesn't seem to harm them though and your chickens remain safe, but maybe just a little startled. To prevent dogs, cats, and foxes from getting to the meat birds, cut lengths of 1x1-inch welded wire one foot wide, and as long as your chicken tractor. Lay the lengths of welded wire flat on the ground along each side of the chicken tractor and attach them to the tractor with zip ties. Cut the wire so bare ends stick out every inch along the outside length of the wire. Now anything that tries to dig under the tractor gets a prick in the nose from the bare ends. Foxes especially find the extra one foot of digging not worth the trouble. Most dogs will stop trying to dig as

Red fox hunt during day and night, are very intelligent, and can be a significant threat to your birds.

Laying some welded wire along the perimeter of your chicken tractor prevents predators from digging under.

soon as they hit the wire lying on the ground. I haven't lost a single bird to a predator since I employed this technique. When it's time to move the tractor, simply fold the lengths of welded wire up against the sides of the tractor and secure them to the chicken wire sides with a few clothespins. When the tractor is in its new location, remove the clothespins and let the welded wire fall back to the ground.

Laying hens

I've seen many ways to protect laying hens and the eggs they provide. I don't think there is a wild critter out there that doesn't want a fresh egg whenever it can get it. You might lose an egg every now and then to a snake. Rats are also known to chew into the side of an egg and lap up the contents. There isn't a whole lot you can do about some of these small egg thieves, but you can protect the hens from larger predators. One option is to keep all your birds locked up in a barn or other outbuilding. That's not necessarily a good thing for folks that want the best quality eggs, but it will work. A second option is to provide access to the outdoors from your outbuilding or chicken coop into a wire enclosure. The enclosure must be completely covered with wire to keep out some intelligent critters like hawks, raccoons, and foxes. When I built my chicken coops, I just happened to have a lot of scrap pieces of 2x10-foot boards left over from building my horse barn. I had a problem with a fox digging under the coop at night and stealing a bird or two. I laid the boards flat on the ground along all sides of the coop. The fox tried only one more time to dig under and gave up way before reaching the coop wall. I haven't lost a bird from the coop at night since then and nothing else has tried to dig under.

Protecting free-ranging chickens provides plenty of challenges but I have discovered a way to defeat each predator so far. The most important thing is to make sure your chickens are put in a well-secured coop every night. Make sure the door and any windows are secured before dark. Dusk is when the nighttime predators begin to move and the longer the birds are outdoors as the sky darkens, the greater chance they will become dinner to some wild and woolly creature. When left outdoors at night, they are easy prey as they sleep. During daylight hours, hawks can sometimes be a problem, especially with smaller chickens. Hawks, owls, eagles, and other predatory birds are a protected species, so harming them in any way is out of the question, unless you're willing to pay a very hefty fine and spend a little time in jail. The larger the chickens you raise, the less likely aerial predators will get them.

I also believe in having several large roosters free-ranging with the chickens. They are very vigilant and give warning to the hens when any threat is around. These techniques have kept all my chickens safe from overhead predators for years even though we have two pairs of Red-tailed hawks nesting on the farm every year. Most other wild predators snooze during the day and are little threat to free-ranging birds. One exception is the red fox — it hunts day and night. One summer, I lost half my flock with a bird taken every other day in the middle of the afternoon. I never saw the fox, just a pile of feathers where it caught each chicken. A pile of feathers is a telltale sign of fox predation.

The solution: I installed a radio near the coop, turned it to a talk radio station, and cranked the volume to high. I turn it on every morning when I let the birds out of the coop and turn it off when I put the birds up at night. Foxes, and maybe some other predators as well, think there are people around, so they stay away. This method has proved 100% successful for the past two years for me even though my birds are ranging over about two acres, both in pasture and woods.

Doves and pigeons

These feathered flyers are best protected with a strong coop and attached wired-in flyway. In addition to all the other predators chickens have, doves and pigeons are susceptible to rats and mice. They both prey mainly on the eggs, but rats will take young birds from the nest, too. I have built coops for both doves and pigeons here on the farm. To keep these pint-sized predators out, I laid out metal lath (the kind used for backing when installing cultured stone) on any bare ground the birds could touch and then covered it with construction sand or limestone sand. Nothing can dig up under your coop and get through the lath without being torn to shreds. The lath has very sharp edges and is so tightly woven it will keep even the smallest mouse out. Cover the outside of your flyway with ½x½-inch welded wire. The small mesh wire not only keeps mice out, but also snakes, which will eat the eggs and young birds.

Quail

Quail should be raised in pens, off the ground, and in a secure building. The building doesn't have to be a walled-in barn or shed; just a simple building with a strong roof and completely wired-in sides will work. I have a small 8x8-foot pole building with plastic roof panels to let in light. All sides are open to outside air but are wired in with ½x1-inch welded wire. I keep incubators, brooders, and rearing and breeding pens all under one roof, providing a smorgasbord for would-be predators. During winter, I tack up a few sheets of plywood on the sides to keep cold drafts out. With this type of building, I have never had a problem with snakes, which really like a nice quail dinner every once in a while. Lath on the floor covered with sand as described above will keep out mice and rats. I've had problems with mice

Strong, well-built coops with heavy welded-wire flyways are excellent protection for a variety of outdoor birds, including doves and pigeons.

eating quail eggs right in the pen. Originally, I only wired in the bottom two thirds of the building. I began having raccoon raids at night that left me with a half dozen headless quail each morning. I finally wired in the remaining openings and this solved the problem and should keep any other critters from getting in. A trail camera pointed at the building has since photographed dogs, cats, foxes, raccoons, opossums, and skunks trying without success to gain entry.

Bigger predators

No matter what type of birds you are raising outdoors, there are a lot of hungry predators looking for an easy meal. Make those meals hard to get and the predators most likely will go elsewhere in search of dinner. Large predators like bears can break through any building you put up. If they are a potential problem for you, try storing your feed away from the coops and buildings where your birds stay. Bears will usually settle for the feed and maybe that's all they're after. I had one bear crush a chicken tractor while trying to get to the feeders inside. Finally, he found a bucket I was storing feed in near the tractor. He hauled the bucket off about 100 yards into the woods and chowed down, leaving my chickens unharmed. In pigeon and dove coops where a lot of waste seed is left on the ground in the coops, it's a good idea to surround the coop with strong electric fencing that will pack a big wallop to any bear nose that touches it. Bears most likely won't bother the birds; but ripping a hole in your flyway to gain entry will certainly be enough to release them all.

Coyotes and domestic dogs can be a problem to most any bird. Strong welded wire on your coops and chicken yards will help keep canines at bay. Keeping a well-trained dog of your own on the property goes a long way in deterring most any predator. Keep your feed in a separate building than your birds and clean up waste feed when you can. Build strong structures from the ground up and use whatever physical barriers you need to keep hungry critters away from your flocks. Employing these simple concepts should help your birds live long and prosper.

The $50 hen house

By Karen M. House

So you want to get some chickens, but don't have a lot of money to spend. The materials you need to build a hen house may be right around you.

When a friend of ours suggested our two families go in together on a flock of laying hens, we started brainstorming about how to build a chicken house with our limited resources. In the end, I designed the building, both families chipped in what we had available in the way of building materials, and the two men built the hen house with just two days of labor.

The first step was to determine how big the building should be. According to the book *Raising Poultry the Modern Way* by Leonard S. Mercia, heavy layers need about two square feet of housing per bird. We planned on raising about 20-30 chicks, so we decided to make the floor space 8 by 8 feet, but with an outdoor exercise yard.

Another consideration was the fact that we live on property that does not belong to us, so the men decided to build the house on skids, allowing it to be moved to another location if need be.

A few features I wanted in the construction included: wire flooring under the roost so the droppings would fall through, a small entrance for the hens to go in and out to the exercise yard, nests accessible for egg collection from the outside, and as much security against predators as humanly possible.

While the men discussed how to go about building the hen house, I went to Tractor Supply and bought our chicks: nine Buff Orpington pullets, nine Plymouth Barred Rock pullets, and two straight-run Black Australorps. We hoped to get at least one rooster out of those straight-run Australorps!

The chicks went in a large box in the living room, with a heat lamp and a ready supply of water and "chick grower" feed.

Happy hens go to roost for the night in their new home.

Terry (left) and Tom begin construction on the hen house with recycled lumber to frame up and some leftover scraps of tin for the roof.

The walls are made of recycled one-inch thick lumber. Half the floor was made of boards, the other half of hardware cloth.

Poles for the roosts were gathered from the woods nearby. Most were dry cedar poles, identified by the red color of the heartwood and its distinctive fragrance. Cedar is desirable in a hen house for repelling insects.

As our plans progressed, the men began to analyze what building materials were already available to them and what would have to be bought.

Our son works on a construction crew with his father-in-law, who has a house across the street from us. As they tear out decks to build new ones, they bring the used lumber up to his house across the street. He stacks it up to use in building projects, and anything he can't use he burns. Having secured permission to use wood from a couple of the stacks, my husband Terry went over to take a look at what was there.

As we loaded boards in Terry's truck, he laughed.

"This lumber would have cost us hundreds of dollars new!" he said. He stacked the lumber next to our house, and the next sunny day he had free he started knocking nails out of the boards.

Tom, our friend and co-conspirator on the hen house project, said he had some odd pieces of tin roofing left from building his house, so he brought that over, and about the time the chicks were getting their feathers, construction began.

Tom and Terry framed up the hen house to my specs, using the recycled lumber. When they needed a different size piece than what they had, they ripped a board or cut it shorter, using the Skilsaw. The walls, likewise, were made from the boards. A hole was cut in the front wall to accommodate three nests, which were built and attached to the wall.

At my insistence, the men enlarged the lip on the inside of the three nests from two inches to four inches, to keep the straw from falling out (a pet peeve of mine with previous flocks of layers).

We compromised on the floor. I had wanted hardware cloth for most of the floor, to keep conditions sanitary. Not only can accumulated droppings increase the hazard of disease to the chickens, they can also carry such diseases as histoplasmosis, which can infect humans. In the end, the men put hardware cloth in the area under the roost, where most of the drop-

Terry and Tom secure the nests in the wall with screws. The hinged lid means eggs can be gathered from the three nests without having to go inside the hen house. The two hinges came from a door salvaged from the dump, with heavy aluminum wire cut to length serving as the pins in the hinges.

pings would fall, and made the front half of the floor out of boards, to give solid footing to anyone who needed to go in the building.

I went out in the woods to see what I could gather to use for roosts. Before heading out, I measured the space and then took the tape measure with me to make sure I got poles that were the right size. I easily located several pieces of long, straight deadwood on the forest floor. Cutting them just a little longer than the right size with a small hand saw, I dragged back to the construction site one piece of maple and three cedars — all dry and hard, and just the right thickness for an adult chicken to comfortably grasp.

If I had realized the cedars were so easy to find, I would have gotten all cedars, because the cedar helps repel insects. As it was, Terry quickly cut and installed the poles I'd found, attaching them to two 1-by-4 boards he'd nailed at a 45-degree angle on each side, over the hardware-cloth floor.

Tom provided an old door, and the bits of tin for the roof. The tin was nailed on, a piece at a time, starting at the lower back end of the roof and overlapping as they went up toward the front. There were well over a dozen bits of tin, but with sufficient drop to the roof, and put on overlapping as they did, the roof has never leaked.

When the nests were installed on the front wall, the men cut a small piece of scavenged quarter-inch plywood for the lid. We had some big, heavy doors we'd rescued from the dump to use on cold frames, and Terry took the hinges off these to put on the nest lid. He cut a piece of heavy aluminum wire he had on hand for the pins to go in the hinges. The men added a nice curved edge to the lid so no one would be hurt bumping into the edge, which was next to the door.

A good overhang to the roof protects the building from the elements, and a larger three-foot overhang at the front protects the person gathering eggs on a rainy day. A scrap of hardware cloth left over from the floor was put over a gap at the top of one wall, which allows air circulation from the eastern side. A 1x1-foot opening at floor level was cut to give the chickens access to the exercise yard.

The hen house was built sitting on small pillars of rocks, but the skids will allow it to be easily moved and transported to another location. Tom contributed an unused dog kennel for the exercise yard, which was bolted securely to the side of the chicken house.

All that remains is to hang the door and install the nests. The skids are visible under the chicken house and will allow the building to be moved to a new location, should the need arise.

With their new home finished, our 6-week-old chicks were introduced to the chicken house. I moved the heat lamp out there with an extension cord, because the nights were still pretty cool. I took one side off the cardboard box that had been their first home and set it on the floor of the hen house, right under the lamp. That gave them a corner in which to cuddle, and a wall against the wind that might blow in through the little chicken door and sometimes up through the wire floor under the roost.

Now, some weeks later, all our chickens are alive and well, and thriving in our little hen house. The only expense in construction was some nails and the hardware cloth, which amounted to a little less than $50. Total construction time was about two days.

We learned a couple of important lessons on this project — first, use what you have to build what you need, and second, a job shared with friends makes it easier to overcome obstacles and is more fun in the doing.

The north wall of the chicken house is solid, to prevent cold winter winds from blowing in. The roof was pieced together from more than a dozen bits of leftover roofing tin. The chain-link fence on the right was an old dog kennel, that we now use to provide the chickens with room to run.

Controlling airborne predators

By Charles Sanders

Chickens sometimes fall prey to a hawk or owl that learns that chickens aren't exactly stealthy in their habits. Occasionally on the homestead, you might discover a casualty or missing member of the flock as you go out to feed or gather eggs. To predators, chickens are convenient, meal-sized critters that are fairly easy to grab.

Food habits vary greatly among hawks and owls. They are all highly specialized predators that take their place at the top of the food chain. As such, some are responsible for the loss of poultry or small game. In decades past, raptors were persecuted through indiscriminate shooting, poisoning, and pole trapping. Today, folks have generally developed an appreciation for these predatory birds and realize that not every bird will become a chicken-killer. Conversely, there are many people who believe that we have overprotected hawks and owls. Many poultry raisers are among this group. If you have ever had a hawk make off with a pullet or kill a prize hen, then your feelings might lean that way, too.

Great horned owl

First off, let's deal with a common misconception. One term that gets thrown around is that of "chicken hawk." Chicken hawk was a term used generically to identify raptors, especially hawks, but has fallen out of usage during the past two or three decades. To many people, every hawk is a chicken hawk. However, there is no such bird. There are chickens and there are hawks, but folks, there just ain't no chicken hawks.

If you or a friend are having a problem with a hawk picking off your poultry, a likely culprit is a Cooper's hawk, Sharp-shinned hawk, or Red-tailed hawk. All three of them are opportunistic hunters and may try to latch onto free-ranging poultry if they get a chance. Great horned owls are the most common owl that is capable of preying on chickens.

Most country folks know that raptors of all types do a lot of good on the farm by way of greatly reducing the numbers of mice and other rodents on the place. So, the first thing to note if you are having problems with a marauding raptor is that the particular bird doing the damage is the one that should be dealt with. Individual birds of the species should be dealt with just so, as individuals, and landowners should not issue blanket death warrants for all birds of prey.

Poultry raisers who experience raptor damage problems should immediately seek infor-

If you are having a problem with a hawk picking off your poultry, a likely culprit is a Cooper's hawk, Sharp-shinned hawk, or Red-tailed hawk.

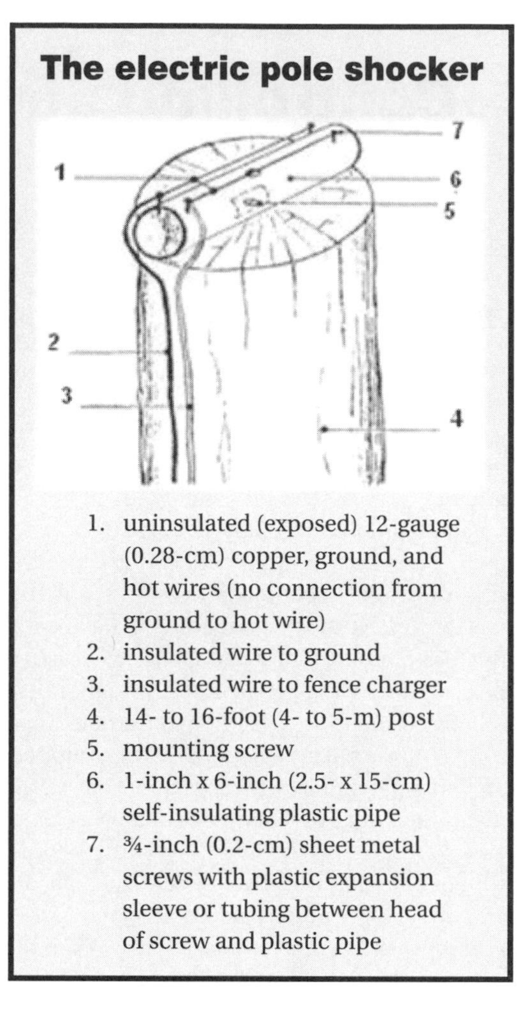

mation and/or assistance. Frustration killings occur far too often because landowners are unfamiliar with or unable to control damage with nonlethal control techniques. These killings result in the needless loss of raptors, and they may lead to undesirable legal actions. If trapping or shooting is necessary, permits should be requested and processed as quickly as possible. Always consider the benefits that raptors provide before removing them from an area; their ecological importance, aesthetic value, and contributions as indicators of environmental health may outweigh the economic damage they cause.

Generally speaking, all hawks and owls are protected by federal and state laws, including the Migratory Bird Treaty Act (16 U.S.C. 703-711). These laws strictly prohibit the capture, killing, or possession of hawks or owls without a special permit. Fish and wildlife officers take these laws pretty seriously. That said, every officer I've known is usually sympathetic to a poultry raiser's plight and will try to help solve the problem. State regulations differ, so do be certain to contact your local state fish and wildlife officer for your available options before controlling offending raptors.

No permits are usually required to simply scare hawks or owls except for endangered or threatened species including bald and golden eagles.

To protect poultry, one of the best methods to reduce or prevent raptor depredation is to simply keep the poultry penned up. You may also opt to cover the pen to protect the birds from above. A light nylon netting made for the purpose can be stretched atop the chicken run and should help put a lid on the depredation.

Sometimes, even that isn't enough. If, like us, you prefer to allow your birds to run outside the pen and forage on their own, then they are more susceptible to depredation by hawks and owls.

Some people employ mobile pens called "chicken tractors" in which to house their flocks. A chicken tractor is simply a small covered chicken pen on wheels. They come in every size and style imaginable and are limited only by the imagination of the homesteader. The movable pens are good in that they can be moved every few days to allow the birds to forage on fresh turf and to better distribute their droppings.

If the poultry pen is very large and covering it is not practical, a device called a pole shocker depicted in the accompanying drawing can help discourage marauding birds. The pole shocker basically provides two wires mounted on a short piece of PVC pipe as an "open circuit." When the raptor lands on the pole, its foot completes the circuit and gives it a good shock, causing it to seek a less painful perch. Obviously, this will be helpful only if there are no other handy perches in the area.

Take a look at the diagram and you can see that a short piece of PVC pipe is attached to the top of a 15- to 20-foot pole. Attached to that piece of PVC pipe is a ground wire and a wire connected to the business end of an electric fence charger. Strip any insulation from the portions of the wires that are attached to the PVC pipe. Small screws provide attachment points for the wires, which are then run down the pole to the charger and to ground. A hole in the center of the pipe allows for attaching the pipe to the top of the post.

If flock confinement, net coverings, and pole shockers do not work, then lethal means may have to be employed. Sometimes, there are cases in which hawks or owls can create public health and safety hazards or seriously affect a person's livelihood. In those cases, a shooting permit may be sought. Contact your local fish and wildlife agency to do that. The USFWS and state wildlife agencies have the latitude to issue shooting permits for problem hawks and owls if nonlethal methods of controlling damage have failed or are impractical and if it is determined that killing the offending birds will alleviate the problem. A potential downside in this process is the time it might take to get the permit. So be sure to contact officials at the first indication that other deterrents haven't worked. Any hawks or owls that are killed must be turned over to U.S. Fish & Wildlife Service personnel or their representatives for disposal. Special permits are required to possess any hawk or owl, alive or otherwise, and those permits are normally limited to learning institutions such as schools, libraries, museums, zoos, and so forth.

As a poultry raiser, be aware of the risks that hawks and owl may pose to your flock. Plan and construct your facilities to prevent the problems as much as possible.

Keep your chickens safe

By Jackie Clay-Atkinson

Chickens are easy to care for because of their small size and their minimal feed and housing requirements. Because of this, they are usually the first of our "livestock" to inhabit our homesteads. However, they are vulnerable to a wide variety of accidents and predators.

With a little forethought and extra care you can easily protect them while they provide you with a bounty of eggs and homegrown meat, not to mention years of pleasure and enjoyment from interacting with these entertaining birds.

Common chicken predators

When we think of dangers to our chickens, predators usually come to mind first — those shifty-eyed, bloody-minded predators who stalk our homesteads at night, looking for a tasty meal. Yep, there are some of those around. Weasels, fishers, raccoons, mink, opossums, foxes, coyotes, and owls will sometimes snatch a chicken or even kill the whole flock during the night. But there are daytime stalkers too. Everyone has heard of "chicken hawks" who swoop down and snatch a hen or chick right out of the yard.

Then there are stray dogs (one of the most common chicken predators). At their own home, they are probably someone's wonderful pet. But all too often, dogs allowed to roam at large turn to killing chickens or small livestock. At first it's just the fun of chasing and seeing feathers fly. But soon it escalates into mass murder. It isn't a good thing to shoot your neighbor's dog, even if it is doing damage in your yard; hard feelings can last for generations.

It is better by far to protect your chickens from all predators in the first place.

Fencing

Most folks would rather free-range their birds. True, the chickens are happier roaming where they will, scratching, sunbathing, and clucking in contentment. But the downside of that vision is that free-ranging puts them at great risk. Not only can a wide variety of predators make off with your chickens, but if you live near a road, they can get hit by cars. If you have neighbors, you can bet they won't be happy with chickens sunbathing in their flower beds, scratching up their garden, or pooping on their decks. As a result, some of your chickens may not come home.

Even if you have no neighbors and don't live by a road, free-ranging can be a pain for your family. Your own chickens will happily dig sunbathing depressions in your flowers, eat your ripe tomatoes, and roost on your pickup.

We like the idea of free-ranging birds but don't like the problems. So what we've done is fence our chickens in our orchard. They have immediate access to about an acre of orchard from their coop. They have all the benefits of free-ranging: plenty of fresh grass, clover,

Our chickens happily roam around the orchard.

insects, and dropped fruit to eat; exercise with fresh air and sunshine, long grass to explore, a place to run and play (yes, chickens *do* play!), but they are safely fenced in a six-foot-high fence of 2x4-inch welded wire. Even their coop is fenced in so a predator can't get inside.

Some folks place their chicken coop in the center, between two large garden plots. One year they let the chickens run in one side while the other side is planted with a garden. When the crops have been harvested, the chickens are allowed to run in the garden while the old chicken run is turned into a garden, complete with weed seeds eaten and the soil fertilized. This is another way to let your chickens "free-range" while being safely fenced in.

When fencing poultry, most folks use chicken wire. Unfortunately, most big predators can rip chicken wire to shreds in a few minutes. So chicken wire isn't the best option to fence in poultry.

There is an electrified netting that is very good for fencing chickens in and predators out. But if the wire is shorted out by a stick, branch, or wet grass, the chickens may stay in but it won't keep a predator out.

The two best fencing materials we've found are the 2x4-inch welded wire and chain link. These will keep out all but the largest and most determined predator from fox to dog.

Of course, a 'possum or raccoon can easily scale this fence. So if you live in their territory, simply add a couple of strands of electric wire, using stand-off insulators, about two feet off the ground (to keep grass from shorting it out) and 28 inches high. This will quickly deter any climbers right then and there.

To be absolutely safe, bury the bottom foot of fence in the ground to keep out determined diggers.

Using 8-foot steel T-posts, you can fence a large area such as a garden/orchard/chicken run in a short time.

Luckily, we don't have trouble with hawks and other raptors. But some homesteaders aren't so lucky. If you have neighbors who have lost birds to hawks or eagles, you'll have to consider putting a top on your run. You can use chicken wire or an avian top netting (often sold through poultry hatchery supply catalogs). To hold it up from sagging, most folks either use braced wooden T-posts or they cross the top of the run with 2x4s to support the netting or wire.

We made our run in the orchard six feet high. As of yet, none of our chickens have flown over it and no deer has ever jumped over it to eat our fruit trees. No dog, coyote, or other non-climbing predator can jump it either.

Making the coop safe

To protect our poultry even further, we shut them inside the coop at night. If they are inside, they are less tempting for predators and we do have lots of owls who could swoop down and get a roosting chicken.

As I've said, our coop is fenced with a yard on three sides and the goat shed on the other side so predators cannot get next to the coop. The further away from tempting smells and sounds, the less predators will get excited and try to get into the coop. I've had raccoons chew through a coop door made of one-inch lumber, break a window glass, and dig under a coop wall. I know it was a raccoon because I caught one inside with a dying hen in its mouth.

So, if you can, run the fence all around the coop. If not, be sure to build your coop nice and strong. It doesn't take much to dig footings for a new coop a foot wide and 18 inches or so deep. Mix up cement and pour over fist-sized rocks and rebar and you'll have a cheap, secure footing no predator will dig through. (Be sure to add some bolts while the concrete is wet so you can bolt down your sill plate to the footing.)

While you can make your coop from OSB or fairly lightweight plywood, it's a good idea to use one-inch plywood or boards for at least the lower quarter of the coop. It's much harder to chew through.

We all (chickens included) love windows in our chicken coop. They provide both light and heat in the winter. But if you use windows, either place smaller single pane windows up at shoulder height or use thicker windows such as used patio doors lower down. They'll be

A good coop is secure and ventilated.

harder or impossible to break. As I said, I had a raccoon break a single pane window on one of my chicken coops. You can also fasten sturdy 1x1-inch welded wire over single pane windows as an added safety precaution.

One note: When building your coop, remember that a weasel can squeeze through a hole as small as the end of your thumb. So close off all knotholes and cracks or this efficient predator may put you out of the poultry business.

Coop safety also means keeping your birds warm enough in the winter and safe from heat prostration in the summer. While you can make an insulated chicken coop and/or heat it with a heat lamp in the winter, you can get by with much less even if you live in the cold north country. Just make sure your birds have no drafts, plenty of other feathered company to keep them warm, and deep bedding to scratch around in. We use wood shavings and build up a deeper layer, adding more shavings all during the winter without cleaning the coop. The chickens are happy and singing even when it's 40 degrees below zero.

Summer heat is actually harder for poultry to endure than cold. As summer approaches, be sure your coop has adequate ventilation. Windows or vents on either side of the coop can be opened and left open to keep air moving and to prevent poultry deaths, especially if they are shut in at night and not let outside right away in the morning. When it is extremely hot, a small fan added to one of the windows will also be very much appreciated.

Fresh water should be provided both in the summer and winter. Chickens can dehydrate quite quickly, especially when summer temperatures soar into the 80s and above.

Drowning hazards

Although you should provide fresh water for your birds, be aware that chickens and turkeys, especially their young, are very prone to drowning. I've lost more poultry to drowning throughout the 50-some years I've had poultry, than to all predators combined. Most of these deaths were when my birds were free-ranging throughout livestock pens and pastures.

Chickens will hop up on a deep watering container, such as a livestock watering tank or tub, reach down to drink, then lose their balance and fall in. Chickens cannot swim, so don't allow them access to a watering container they can't stand up in. With chicks and poults, this is very shallow, only a couple of inches maximum. (You'll notice that waterers for baby birds are only an inch deep and so narrow that they can't get in them.)

Chickens will also drown in decorative ponds, livestock ponds, ditches, and even a wheelbarrow full of water. The water attracts them and in they go. It's so sad to find a drowned dead chicken in a container of water. They aren't the brightest and rely on us to think ahead for them. With a little planning and creative construction, your poultry flock will lead a safe and happy life, leaving you free to enjoy every day's interaction with them.

Use dogs to protect chickens

By Karen M. House

It was a scene of tragedy ... a pile of feathers, two orphaned chicks, and a missing hen. Whatever it was that had attacked our free-range flock of chickens while we were gone for the day also had carried off (or swallowed whole) several of the hen's downy chicks.

A search of the local area revealed a hole about 100 yards away that might have been the den of a fox or coyote, but we were not sure. We were relative novices in country living at that point — about 25 years ago.

For country folk, raising a flock of chickens is a constant battle with predators. Whether it's a fox, coyote, opossum, raccoon, hawk, or even somebody's pet dog or cat, predators can whittle away at your flock if you don't take action to stop them.

In the case illustrated above, we soon found out what was after our chickens. I awoke the next night to the sound of chickens cackling in the dark. When chickens cackle in the middle of the night, you can bet your bottom dollar some unwanted intruder is after them.

I opened the front door, flipped on the porch light, and saw Flossy, a light-colored hen that had recently hatched a brood of chicks. She was in the jaws of a fox. The fox paused, gave me an annoyed look, and then dropped the chicken and trotted off into the darkness. Flossy wasted no time, but immediately took advantage of her sudden redemption and raced off in the opposite direction. That night, our blue heeler, Cissy, went from being a pet to a farm dog. She started sleeping outside at night, and we never lost another chicken from that flock.

As for Flossy, we found her later that night, as we searched through the grass with a flashlight. She was alive and appeared unharmed. I carried her back to the hen house and put her back in, where she had been sitting with her chicks on the floor. I locked the chickens up that night, and every night after that.

Next day, though, as dusk drew near, I saw Flossy climbing up on a wooden framework that had been removed from my husband's truck and was sitting in the yard. It was like a wooden fence, maybe 4 feet tall. Flossy cluck-cluck-clucked to her chicks, and one by one they got their fluffy little butts up the framework, until they rested under the wings of their mother on the top rail. That hen was no dummy!

Big predators

Over the years, we've raised half a dozen flocks of chickens. We have lived in close proximity to foxes, hawks, coyotes, even mountain lions and wolves. The chickens we've lost to predators have primarily been taken by fox, hawk, and pet dog.

When we lived in a national forest in Alabama, we had several first-person accounts of one or more mountain lions traveling the area. A mountain lion can live and hunt a 20-mile radius. But even though the lion traveled close to us and our neighbors, they never attacked our animals, which included chickens, goats, a horse, dogs, and cats.

We lived for a short time in west Texas, but before we arrived, our hosts had encountered some aggressive timber wolves that were not native to the area. These wolves had been raised by local breeders, and when the breeders decided to move away, they turned the wolves loose into the desert. These were major predators, used to eating chicken and rabbit, and had no fear of man. The caretaker of the farm was there when four hungry wolves showed up. He quickly locked himself in a small cabin. The wolves devoured the poultry and rabbits, pulling the rabbits through the bars of their cage.

The next day, when the caretaker failed to show up at an expected time, a friend came to check on him. The wolves rushed his truck, and he shot them there in the driveway. When we arrived a few days later to stay on the property, four black smudges still marked where the men had burned the wolf carcasses. Again, these were non-native animals raised by humans. The thoroughly wild red wolves that were native to the area never approached human habitation, as far as I knew.

When we lived off-grid in Tennessee in the late 1990s, we could hear the coyotes go through the valley at night, their yips and howls sounding like demons let out of hell. One night, when I was reading to my children, we stopped to listen to one lone coyote howling on the mountain. Yet, in the three years we lived there we never lost a chicken, pig, goat, calf, or pet to a coyote. We had at least one dog on the premises at all times.

There are people who hunt coyotes, and some states award bounties for coyote pelts, but studies have shown that hunting pressure on coyotes causes a corresponding increase in litter size. Hunting them may, in fact, be counterproductive.

The larger predators seem to give humans a wide berth, unless they've been handled by people and so become unafraid of us. It's been my experience that a human dwelling with free-roaming dogs about will not often be approached by the larger predators.

Smaller predators

Besides the time the fox got Flossy's sister, my greatest problem has been with hawks and dogs.

Hawks are a unique problem, because they can drop in from the sky. Where we live now, there is a pair of broad-winged hawks nesting nearby. I have seen them flying together out over the valley, and even circling high up over our place, but they have never gone after our chickens. A full-sized hen is simply too big for that breed of hawk to carry off.

Even though the small, light-colored hawks have not posed a problem, we recently lost a chicken to a Red-tailed hawk that dropped into our chicken pen and ran a hen into the fence. He pulled her head back through the next hole over, effectively breaking her neck. I heard the chickens cackling and got there in time to prevent the hawk from actually eating the hen, but she was dead anyway.

The first two things I noticed when I ran out the door was a hen walking quickly along the fence inside the pen, cackling loudly, and a blue jay in a tree above her screaming at something. My first thought was that a snake was in the pen, but then I saw the hawk on the ground around the corner of the hen house. I yelled for my husband, and by the time he came out, the hawk had abandoned his chicken dinner and flown up into a nearby tree, with the blue jay harassing him mercilessly. The hawk lifted off and sailed out over the rocky cliff that marks the edge of our mountain.

We tacked the young hen by the feet on a tree in the back yard, and as I was butchering her, I heard the squeal of a hawk and looked over in time to see the big Red-tailed hawk sailing out in the blue with his talons extended. Then I realized there were two hawks screaming. There was one of our local broad-winged hawks, hot on the intruder's tail, with her claws extended, too. The local guys were running off that Red-tail!

That day, we put our Anatolian Shepherd Dog in the pen with the chickens. Anatolians are livestock guardian dogs, and although our dog had been raised with humans as a family guardian, we figured with her in the chicken pen and the local hawks on guard, we stood a better than average chance of avoiding a return attack. So far, we haven't had another predator attack.

Hawks will often conduct "practice raids" on your flock, especially free-ranging poultry, to see where the chickens run when threatened. If you see a hawk cruising low over your flock, sitting in a tree nearby watching them, or otherwise showing undue attention to your chickens, you can be sure the hawk has fresh chicken on the menu!

We've also had our own dogs kill chickens, usually because the birds were something new to them. Strongly correcting a smart dog will usually do the trick. If not, you need to get rid of either the dog or the chickens. The accepted policy in most rural areas is that if my dog kills

One of the best tools for deterring predators is a good fence.

The chicken flock is an investment. Predators can whittle away at profits.

your livestock, my dog has forfeited his life. When my dog kills my livestock, I have more latitude in correcting the problem.

Deterring predators

Generally speaking, the best deterrents to predators are a good dog and a good fence. If your hen house is sturdy with no holes except the door, if your fence has no gaps, and if you have one or two good, protective dogs, predators will normally give your place a wide berth. Remember, the dog has to have access to the yard night and day in order to be effective.

Free-range flocks require a little closer supervision. You might want to pen the birds up if you go to town, and it's always advisable to close them up every night.

Hawks can be deterred if they become a serious problem by tying string across the top of the chickens' exercise yard, crisscrossed to form a net that the hawk would not want to get tangled in. Or you can cover the opening with chicken wire.

Large predatory birds like hawks and eagles — both called raptors — are protected by federal law. Some states will not prosecute you for killing any animal that kills your livestock, but the federal government can and will impose fines of thousands of dollars if they find out you've killed a hawk or eagle.

The ultimate protection for chickens — and all other livestock — is a livestock guardian dog (LGD). There are many breeds of LGD, including Anatolian Shepherd, Great Pyrenees, Kangal, Maremma, and Akbash. All are large, independent-minded dogs that bond with their "family," whether that be people, sheep, goats, or poultry. They will chase off any threatening predator, to the point of laying down their life in the defense of their family. Most of these breeds originated among sheepherders in Asian or Mediterranean lands, where they protected the flock from wolves.

You may not have ever had a problem with predators, but if you raise poultry for any length of time at all, you will. Plan now to protect your investment.

Build an electric metal barrier to protect your chickens

By David A. Williams

A well-constructed charged barrier can eliminate varmint predation of chickens.

Needed in this construction is a fence charger. It may be solar-powered or plugged into an outlet. It must be grounded properly. If you are new to fence chargers, necessary instructions to properly ground, install, and use the charger are provided with the unit. Follow them!

Next, one will need metal roofing or some other metal sheeting at least 24 inches wide, self-tapping sheet metal screws, pliers, a drill to insert the screws, a hammer, a shovel, PVC pipe at least 2 inches in diameter (used pipe works well), long narrow strips of metal, a pair of metal snips, and wire (wire designed for electric fencing works the best).

With the construction of this electrified barrier, one can easily exclude skunks, possums, raccoons, feral cats, dogs, bobcats, foxes, and most importantly to yours truly, rat snakes — known as chicken snakes in central Texas. Not only do they dine on eggs, they also devour chicks.

Yes, I could construct a coop that would entirely preclude these predators, but it would have to be totally enclosed with metal or wood siding. It would get extra hot in the summer. Temperatures in the 95 to 105 degree range for 90 days make it mighty uncomfortable for the hens. Egg production suffers as well. The best bet is to build a chicken house with a solid barrier at the bottom and two feet or more of chicken wire above this, the chicken wire allowing good ventilation and keeping the girls cooler. County extension agents have coop plans which are designed for cooling in the summer and retaining warmth in the winter months.

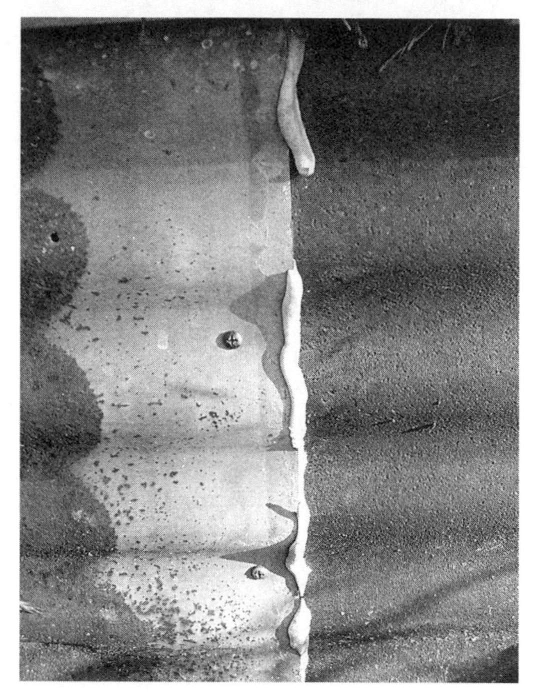

This picture shows the joint where two sheets of grounded 16-inch-tall barrier metal are joined. I applied excess caulk before I took the picture so as to display parts of the joint more prominently.

The principle behind the electrically-charged barrier: Provide a physical barrier that extends eight inches into the ground all the way around the house and the same barrier extending up 16 inches or more above the soil line. This will be hooked directly to the ground side of the charger.

Then, install an electric-fence-charged impediment near the top of the 16-inch section. Grounded by the barrier as they crawl up it, snakes will be shocked away from the coop when they touch the electrified impediment. Four-legged varmints tend to lean one front foot on the barrier, then reach up to the electrified impediment and get the same shock.

To begin, dig an 8-inch-deep trench around the house. Put the metal in this trench — running lengthwise. Follow the soil level so as to keep the top part of the barrier 16 inches above the earth all the way around the house. On the chicken house corners, bend it around the corner and secure it to the next sheet. Caulk this seam. Overlap the sheets and secure the seam well with screws. Do this all the way around the house. When finished, you will have an entry-free metal barrier 16 inches or more tall (depending on the metal you use) above the soil line. I suggest no shorter than 16 inches at any time. Fill the trench with dirt after you have completed securing the metal sheets to each other.

The barrier must completely surround the bottom of the house with the exception of the door.

Corrugated roofing has ridges so when you attach the metal onto the door jamb, you will have open areas between it and these ridges. Fill these with screen wire or whatever is available to preclude snakes from entering the coop via these openings. Corrugated metal ridges can be beaten flat to solve the problem, but it looks ugly. If you use flat sheets of metal, this would not be necessary as there would be no gaps. Remember, the 16-inch-tall barrier must be completely secure from entry.

Next, drill one-inch diameter holes on one side of the PVC 30 inches apart and set the pipe in the topmost groove of the corrugated metal. Insert a sheet metal screw (designated as screw A) through these one-inch holes to the inside wall of the PVC and install A through the inside PVC wall and on into the sheet metal at the top of the barrier. Do this every 30 inches down the length of the metal around the coop. This PVC pipe is the insulator placed between the ground (negative) and the hot (positive) of the barrier. Now, you have an insulated obstacle that is attached securely to the corrugated metal with no gaps between the PVC and the metal. If there are gaps, fill them in with screen wire or whatever you have handy. This must be done to insure a snake or any other small crit-

The eastern side of my chicken house with the barrier complete. Note that the barrier follows the contour of the land — lower at left and rising to the right. This keeps everything at least 16 inches above the soil level.

Here is a close-up of the barrier. You can see the 16-inch-tall corrugated metal barrier in the rear, the used PVC pipe insulating obstacle in the middle (I used odds and ends and spliced them together), and the outer metal strip which is electrified.

A close-up of the barrier viewed from the top of the chicken house

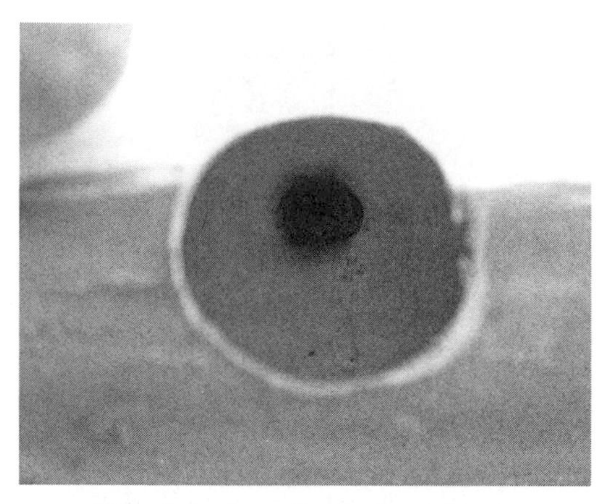

This photo shows the sheet metal screw (screw A) inside the PVC that attaches the PVC to the inner 16-inch-tall grounded barrier.

This is the one-inch diameter hole on the outside of the PVC where one inserts screw A to attach it as in the photo above.

Here is a close-up of a self-tapping metal screw (screw B) used to attach the outer strip to the PVC.

ter can't crawl up the sheet metal and slither between it and the PVC.

The outside wall of the PVC extends two inches from the grounded sheet metal. On this outside wall, attach the strips of metal with sheet metal screws (designated screw B). The B screws and A screws must not touch or they will conduct the electrical charge from the outer strips of metal to the interior grounded barrier. Overlap these small metal strips whenever they meet and around each corner so there will be a constant metal ribbon around the house.

Run an insulated hot wire from the hot side of the charger to the strips on the outside of the PVC and securely attach. Install an "on/off" switch in this wire where it can be easily accessed so one can turn the juice on or off. Then, run an insulated ground wire to the 16-inch-high barrier and attach securely. Both wires should be insulated so the "hot" will never contact the "ground." I use garden hose as the needed insulation. Turn the charger on and the barrier is complete.

Now, the chicken house door. It must shut completely, with no cracks to allow snakes, mice, rats, or other small predators to slip through and evade the carefully assembled electrified barrier. Construct a door that seals as well as the front one of your house. After all, if you have the right to be secure in your own premises, why shouldn't your most valuable livestock have that right as well?

A major tenet of homesteading is prevention. Please remember to shut up your chickens after they go to roost. These few minutes of care prevent headaches later on. Turn the on/off switch off if you will be near the electrified impediment. It shocks all varmints, even two-legged ones. Be sure the barrier is turned on again after you shut up the chickens.

Yes, varmints can enter the coop during the day when the door is open, but if one is vigilant, this problem is minimal. I wait until the hens have laid in the morning and I gather the eggs before I let them out. If a snake happens along, he misses a meal. Also, if the girls observe a predator, they usually set up a fuss and I deal with the intruder.

When correctly installed, field mice and rats cannot get inside at night to dine on the girls' feed. For the last 10 years, I have never had any critter dig under the 8-inch-deep metal barrier nor get inside the chicken house as long as the impediment was charged. I lost no chickens to predators during this decade. My feed bill declined as well.

This is how I constructed the barrier. I am sure it can be built differently in other situations, but the principle of shocking varmints to keep them out of the coop is the key.

Build a doghouse chicken coop

By Kari Kelley

We got a starter coop for a good deal on Craigslist and the seller threw in two free hens. This worked well for several weeks, but we knew we wanted to expand our flock and the starter coop would only fit about six chickens. Then, within the space of a week, we went from two hens to seven hens and two roosters. It was time for a new coop!

Luckily, we had just gotten a free wooden doghouse from a friend. It was in rough shape: the light blue paint peeling off the wood sides, accumulated dirt and debris inside, and let's not forget the many wasp nests (though thankfully empty). However, the thing was solid and the shingled, peaked roof did not leak. There was an arched door cut out of the front that came with a sliding cover. Overall, the doghouse measured about 3x4x3½ feet and it seemed to weigh slightly less than a ton.

The first job was to clean out the inside, but with the peaked roof and small door (a mere 14x16 inches), I couldn't reach all the angles to knock down the empty wasp nests. Nor could I entirely get the debris from the front corners. So, I asked my husband if he would cut a door in the back. He told me to mark where I wanted

We keep the front door of the coop open during the day and closed at night.

The back of the coop has holes for ventilation at the top.

Here, our New Hampshire Red is checking for food. I placed a small waterer inside the coop for overnight use, and the back door is wide enough to facilitate cleaning out the coop.

it cut, and he would cut it. There was about 3½ inches between the ground and the floor of the doghouse, so I had to make sure the bottom of the door was above that. The opening that was cut out ended up being 24x20½ inches. My husband then screwed 2x4s to the inside of the wood to make it sturdier since it would be opened and closed quite a bit. Then he put thin two-inch pieces of wood around three edges, to stop the door from swinging in and also to keep drafts from coming in through the cracks. We had leftover hinges from another project and screwed those on, then added a knob we also had from another project. A metal clasp to keep the door closed finished that part of it.

My husband figured there should be some means of ventilation in the new coop, so he cut 2x8-inch holes in the top front and back, just under the peak. He put chicken wire over the opening and then anchored it with small pieces of wood screwed on the top and bottom of the opening. We used an old shelf for the ramp and nailed on wood strips for the chickens to grasp. We decided we wanted the coop off the ground, so he cut six 16-inch rounds from old fence posts that we had gotten free on Craigslist, and screwed those to the inside bottom (since there was that clearance between the ground and floor of the coop). He then braced those with 2x4s around the outside. All the wood and other parts we used were leftovers from other projects and we had the nails and screws on hand, so the chicken coop cost us virtually nothing.

The chickens love taking dust baths under the coop, or even just using it for shade. Our three Chanteclers use it at night, though all the chickens wander in and out during the day. Since the other coop is at max capacity with six chickens, the three Buckeye hens I'm getting tomorrow will fit in the doghouse chicken coop just fine!

Build a chicken "bunker"

By Brad Rohdenburg

We live in a neighborhood that some people might not feel is appropriate for chickens. How can anyone not appreciate birds that turn insects and kitchen waste into fertilizer and breakfast?

We bend over backwards to stay on good terms with our neighbors. Because, you know, we might have to live next to them or something. So we wanted our coop to not only shelter our little flock from wind, rain, cold, heat, and predators, but also to be visually unobtrusive, and to muffle the sound of a rooster.

We decided to build an earth-sheltered coop — partially below-grade, with earth-bermed walls and a sod roof. Earth-sheltering blocks the wind and moderates temperatures in all seasons with thermal mass. A sod roof is maintenance-free and provides evaporative cooling on hot summer days. It was more work than a conventional shelter, but it's camouflaged so well that most people don't even realize that it's there until I point it out. And our rooster sounds significantly less like a foghorn.

Start by digging a hole — a big hole. A lot bigger than you think you need.

Hopefully you'll have a neighbor with a backhoe who will feel sorry for you when he sees you digging by hand.

Then build a log cabin, underground. These pressure-treated timbers are notched so that the weight of the backfilled dirt will hold them together. There are no fasteners.

The framework must be engineered to support the load, which includes the weight of the structure itself; the weight of earth satu-

rated with water (about 10 pounds per square foot for every inch); and the snow load you should anticipate (ask local officials; mine is 70 pounds per square foot). The help desk at the local building supply store did the calculations for me.

Drainage is the better part of waterproofing. If you provide an easier place for rainwater to go than into your coop, it will go there. The ground has been sloped away from the walls to help channel water away, along with four-inch diameter perforated pipes covered with filter cloth and buried in a bed of crushed rock along the perimeter.

The roof is pitched at 1 foot of vertical rise in 12 feet of horizontal run. This is enough to allow water to run off, without the sod roof sliding off.

We decked the roof with 1½-inch-thick pressure-treated lumber.

Then we covered it with a waterproof roofing membrane. Just as an insurance policy, we also added a layer of 6-mil black plastic.

We covered the windows and the door with welded hog panels, to keep out large predators, and then with chicken wire, to keep out small ones.

For the finishing touches, we covered the earth berms and roof with compost.

The interior has nesting boxes and several levels of roosts. From a chicken's point of view, vertical space is just as good as floor space. Speaking of which, the floor of our coop is just dirt covered in wood shavings, pine needles, straw, and shredded leaves. The hens scratch in the litter and keep it mixed and aerated. Worms eat it from the bottom. (Bait for fishing is never a problem for us.) Occasionally, we pitchfork the bedding out the door and onto the roof, then replace it with fresh.

If you don't have well-drained soil and/or a way to divert water, a below-grade coop may not be a viable option. But even an above-grade coop can have waterproofed walls with earth bermed up against them. And I think that a sod roof is always a great option for small outbuildings. It will last longer than you will, because the earth protects the waterproofing membrane from the sun. In the summer, the plants growing on it provide shade and evaporative cooling. In the winter, the blanket of fluffy snow is a good insulator. And last, but not least, a living roof planted with wildflowers is beautiful.

PROJECTS

Starting a hen saddle business

By Jill Bong

Jill's homesteading adventures began when she and her husband bought their new (old) house and set up a small homestead on the Rocky Mountain Foothills. The mainstay of their homestead was having a large flock of more than 80 chickens. Like other chicken hobbyists, they had problems with frisky roosters and hens pecking at each other.

One device to help alleviate pecking and scratching problems is a "hen saddle," also known as a chicken apron. A hen saddle is a cape-like device that is placed on a hen's back. It is held on by straps which run under the chicken's wings. The saddle is traditionally sewn from tough material such as canvas or denim.

Jill could sew them herself (there are numerous online sites with instructions on how to make them), or she could buy them. Since she had a large flock, Jill had a threefold problem:

1. It would be too expensive to saddle more than 3-4 chickens.
2. It would be too much work to sew them herself.
3. The canvas, denim, or cloth material used would be too much of a hassle to launder.

The couple was not satisfied with the use of traditional material, so they racked their brains to find something that could be easily cleaned but did not need to be sewn. After trying many samples from dealers, they finally decided on a reinforced vinyl material: it was cheap, it did not fray when cut, it could be hosed down easily, and it was tough and made for outdoor use.

The couple worked on various prototype designs and finally settled on a design that was easy to cut but still allowed the saddle to stay on the chicken. The final design allowed them to make the saddles at home. The saddles worked so well for their own flock that they decided start selling them for a reasonable price of $10 for 10 saddles.

Saddle instructions

This can be made using any thick material strong enough to withstand the coop.

The straps are elastic. They can be attached with buttons, or the top panel can be lengthened a little more, folded over, and sewn so that a one-piece elastic can be pulled through. The lower ends of the elastic can be fastened with buttons.

The design is meant to fit a standard-sized chicken.

Selling on a shoestring budget

The first sales came from posting free ads on niche forums online. The first saddles were

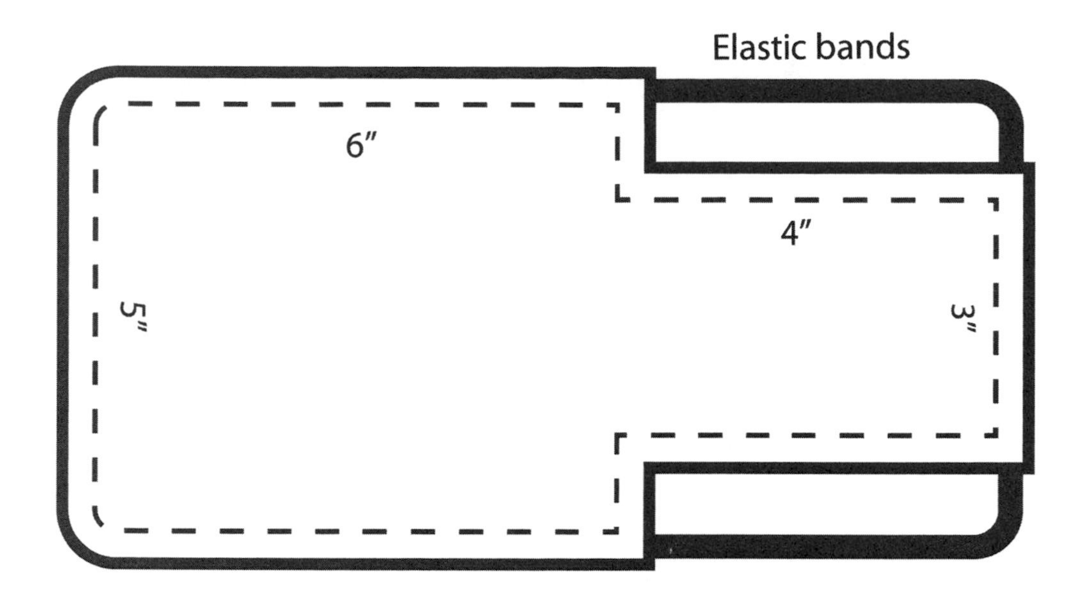

made from sample material provided by dealers.

With the initial revenue, the couple invested in more material and started selling on eBay and Etsy. They also set up a no-frills online storefront for free using www.freewebstore.org.

As sales started rolling in, the couple took important steps to protect their business and the invention. They registered their company as a limited liability company (LLC), doing business under the brand "Chicken Armor."

Jill found inspiration and marketing ideas from a fellow homesteader and writer, Anna Hess, author of *Microbusiness Independence: How to Quit Your Job and Start to Live*. She gave Jill the idea of writing articles for poultry magazines. Each article gave Chicken Armor more exposure and increased sales.

To protect their idea, Jill looked into applying for a provisional patent (which is cheaper than a regular patent and protects your invention temporarily). However, she decided that it would be more cost-effective to simply apply for a patent on their chicken saddles.

The initial application was rejected and Jill decided it would be best to hand the application over to a patent attorney. As of the date of this writing, Chicken Armor's hen saddles are still in the patent-pending stage.

Since 2012, Chicken Armor has sold more than 10,000 chicken saddles worldwide, helping homesteaders on a budget saddle their own chickens. Chicken Armor hen saddles can be purchased on Jill's website at www.chickenarmor.com.

Build a chicken treat box

By Carol Freiberg

My hens live beneath my rabbits, so any food I give my girls has to have a lid to protect the contents from the droppings of the upstairs tenants. I already have a cover for their hen chow, but I needed something to both hold and cover their special cracked corn they covet. So I figured out a way to build a protected, self-serve chicken treat box.

Parts list:

- 1 base platform (12x12-inch square 1-inch thick)
- 1 pine board (¾-inch thick and 36 inches long)
- 4 carriage bolts (¼ x 2-inch long)
- 4 carriage bolts (¼ x 1½-inch long)
- 16 washers (¼-inch)
- 8 lock nuts (¼-inch)
- 2 extra small screw eyes
- 1 1½-inch spring
- 30 1¼-inch deck screws

Tools needed:

- jig saw or circular saw to cut wooden pieces
- drill with a 9/16-inch bit for counter sinking holes, a ¼-inch bit for bolt holes, and a 1/16-inch bit for pre-drilling screw holes
- sandpaper to smooth edges

Lay out and cut all pieces as follows:

1- bottom of box (5 x 7 inches)

2- sides of box (¾ x 5 x 7 inches). In the sides, cut notch in corner that measures ¾ x 3¾ inch-

Lid Lifter
Side
2
Bottom
Front
Lid
4½" x 7"
Front
Step
2½" x 7"
Side
3/4" x 5" x 7"
notch
3/4" x 3 3/4"
1¼" from
edges of
side
piece

es. Lay inside up and drill counter sunk hole on the front end (the un-notched end) of the side piece 1¼ inches from the front and bottom edge. Counter sink a second hole on the notched end of box, 2¼ inches up from the bottom edge, and ¾ inch in from the back edge.

- 1 front of box (5 x 5¾ inches)
- 1 back of box (5 x 5 inches)
- 1 back lid piece (3¾ x 5 inches)
- 1 front lid that opens (3½ x 7 inches)
- 2 wedges (cut a ¾ x 1¼ x 4-inch block diagonally to make the two wedges)
- 1 step (2½ x 7 inches)
- 2 side arms (¾ x 1 x 9½ inches.) At the bottom of each arm, cut a notch that measures 2½ x ¾ inches for step piece. On inside of arm pieces, counter sink one hole that's centered and ¾ inch from the end. Go upwards 3½ inches and drill another ¼-inch hole.
- 2 lifter arms (¾ x 1 x 7½ inches.) On inside of pieces, counter sink one hole 3 inches from the back end and drill a ¼-inch hole that's centered ¾ inch from back end of piece.
- 2 hinge boards (1x ⅜ x 3¾ inches). Drill a ¼-inch hole ¾ inch from each end.

Now that it's cut and drilled, it's time to assemble. Remember to use the 2-inch bolts

My coop is below my rabbit hutch.

to go through the sides of the box, and the 1½-inch bolts to hold the hinge on.

Push the 1½-inch bolts through the counter sunk holes in the lifter arms and the side arms. Place washer on bolt, followed by hinge board, another washer, and lock nuts. Place the 2-inch bolts through box from the inside out. Add a washer. Now, place the joined arm/lifter pieces onto the 2-inch bolts, followed by washers and lock nuts. Attach the step piece to the notched end of arms. Screw down the back lid to top of box. Screw wedges to front end of lifter arms. Lay front lid on top and attach with deck screws.

Set box onto platform and use deck screws to hold in place. The tiny screw eyes are attached 2½ inches from the front end of one of the lifter arms, and the second screw eye 6 inches from the front of the step. Add the spring and secure with pliers. The tension can be adjusted if needed so that one hen's weight can open the box and still not cause injury to another hen's neck who may be eating when she steps off. After three days of training (mostly me opening the box with a rake handle), at least two of my six hens had it figured out. In a week's time, all could open the box and enjoy cracked corn. Once you have accomplished this project, you may want to adapt it for other uses.

Just enjoy your afternoon making something your hens will love you for!

Simple chicken toys and treats

By Nell Davidsen

Because I am a homesteader who also has a full-time job, my flock sometimes gets the short end of the stick when it comes to attention. Sure, I always get them fresh water and top off their feed before I leave for the day, but they have to wait for the weekend for quality entertainment. On the weekend, my husband and I let them out to free-range, give them buckets of weeds from the garden, and we even give each hen some cuddle time.

However, I can't help but feel guilty for all the days in-between when I am at work. I felt like I needed to find cost-effective ways to entertain my slightly-spoiled flock when I wasn't there. So I started looking into do-it-yourself toys and treats.

DIY toys

I have a raised coop, with nesting boxes and a roost on top, and a small run underneath where I keep my chickens' food and water. The small run opens into a larger run surrounded by chain-link fence and covered with wire. The flock has the whole run of the place, but it's pretty flat and boring.

The first thing I did was wedge a rounded piece of scrap wood in the corner of the chain-link run about three feet above the ground. The chickens love to take turns jumping up there! Even the rooster will jump up, let out a loud cock-a-doodle-doo, then jump back down. Two of my hens are inseparable, and they both sit up there at the same time, cackling happily to each other.

My chickens love to scratch. If there's any pile of anything, they want to level it (while searching for bugs, of course). They've decimated my compost pile during free-range more times than I care to admit. To add entertainment during the weekday, I like to throw a small pile of straw in the middle of their run. Since we use straw for their bedding, we've always got plenty of it.

This "treat roller" costs nothing to make.

A chicken perch adds excitement.

For this treat, I first added some weeds from my flower bed.

Then, I added some blueberries that were all wrinkled from being in the fridge too long.

Another easy and cheap way to add entertainment to your run is to throw an old ball in there. The chickens will roll it around in a mini-game of soccer. Just make sure that the ball is made of material strong enough to resist pecking — if you throw a nerf ball in there, bored chickens might start eating away at it.

Chickens love anything new in their coop, so every once in a while, I'll put a big rock or an old stump in there. An added benefit is when I move it or take it out, the chickens go crazy pecking at all the bugs that made their home underneath.

I topped it off with a shriveled diced carrot, then filled the pan with water and put it in the freezer.

The chickens love their frozen treat!

A lettuce "tetherball" keeps the chickens busy for an hour or two. In the background, you can see a stump that I put in for entertainment.

DIY treats

Let's face it; the easiest way to entertain a chicken is to simply give it food. But there are ways to make it more of a challenge for the chickens. Here's how you can make a fun treat feeder. First, get a plastic bottle (I usually get an old water bottle, but any cylindrical bottle will do). Now, poke holes in the sides large enough for whatever feed you are putting in there to fall through — I don't make large holes, as I put in cracked corn scratch. Unscrew the cap, fill the bottle with the food, then put the cap back on. When you put this "treat roller" in the run, the chickens will kick and scratch at it, which will release small amounts of treats.

Another way to make the chickens work for their food is to make a "chicken tetherball." First, buy or grow a head of lettuce or cabbage. Using a wire, wrap the head of lettuce, then attach the other end to the top of the run. Make sure it hangs a couple of feet above the ground. The chickens will jump at it to grab a piece, which will send it spinning in another direction. It's fun chaos in the coop, although the lettuce head will be completely gone within an hour or two. This could work with any kind of firm produce – zucchini, corn, etc.

Although chickens don't care what shape their food comes in, sometimes making your

Two days' worth of beautiful eggs from happy chickens

own shaped treats can brighten up your coop and make you feel like a really great chicken owner. I've seen really elaborate treats online made with alfalfa, flaxseed, and organic peanut butter that take a couple hours to make and shape into delicate hearts and wreaths. If that's your thing, go for it, but I doubt I'll ever have time for that! For a quick summer treat that's just as fancy-looking, all you need are some produce leftovers that have been sitting too long in the fridge, water, and a bundt pan. I dump the old produce in my bundt pan (I've used corn, blueberries, kale, spinach, and peas), fill it with enough water to cover the produce, and freeze. Once it's frozen through, I just turn the pan over and give it a good whack. As it melts, the chickens will be able to peck at the produce. This treat is quick to make, uses ingredients that are already on hand, and is a great way to help your flock cool off.

Chickens love to eat almost anything. A few times I've thrown a too-old-for-us-to-eat watermelon into the coop on my way to work, and by the time I came home, there was nothing left. They even ate the rinds! I've also thrown in squash and pumpkins, which are not as big of a hit as a watermelon, but they serve to entertain the flock. Plus, squash and pumpkin seeds are natural chicken dewormers.

Conclusion

Since I've implemented these toys and treats, I see a world of difference in my flock. Entertained chickens don't peck at each other as much, which means there is less squawking coming from my coop. I've also noticed that my hens are laying more eggs. I used to get only four or five on average per day, but now I'm getting seven or eight!

Some might say this is due to the hens' age, or the time of year, but I like to think my girls are saying "thank you" in the only way they know how.

Build an automatic chicken waterer for $20 or less

By Jeanie Woodburn

One of my least favorite chores is changing the chickens' water bucket each morning. It's cold, mucky, and the chickens always manage to scratch a ridiculous amount of manure and dirt into the water. I tried raising up their bucket by setting it on paving stones, but it was still getting too dirty.

So, I started researching alternative ways to water my chickens. The simplest and cheapest way was to build a gravity-fed chicken waterer with poultry "nipples" for the chickens to drink out of. Similar to hamster waterers, these nipples release water when the chicken reaches up to peck at it. When I looked online, I found these nipples were inexpensive and had free shipping, so I decided to go for it.

Materials and costs

- 25-pack of threaded chicken nipples: $6.50 (I only used three of the nipples)
- five-gallon bucket with lid: Free (I already had one)
- one length of 1-inch PVC pipe: $4.29
- three 1-inch elbow attachments: $2.07
- 1-inch male adapter: $0.79
- 1-inch locknut: $0.79
- zip ties: $1.00
- silicone sealant: $4.99

Tools

- PVC cutter (or hacksaw would work)
- 5/16-inch drill bit
- 1-inch spade drill bit

Process

Step 1:

The first thing I did was throw together a little table for the five-gallon bucket to sit on. It has to be a few inches above the watering area. If you don't have a lot of extra scrap wood like I did, you could just balance a piece of plywood on some concrete blocks. The only thing that is necessary is a hole near the middle of the stand. This is where the PVC pipe will go through.

With these tools and materials, you can build an automatic waterer in less than an hour's time.

Step 2:

With my table made, it was time to get the bucket set up. I turned the bucket upside down, then drilled a 1-inch diameter hole right in the center. It ended up being a little bit too small to fit the male adapter, so I sawed around it with a steak knife until I could push the adapter through. Once I pushed the adapter into the bottom, I reached inside the bucket and screwed on the locknut, then set the bucket on the table (with the adapter fitting through the hole).

I built this little table, but almost anything will work.

Fit the male adapter into the bottom of the bucket.

Once the adapter is fitted, screw on the locknut (on right).

Step 3:

Without measuring, I eyed where I wanted the PVC to go, then cut it. The length of pipe with the nipples on it needs to be about the height of your chickens' eyes. Any higher, and they won't drink from it very often — any lower and they will have trouble getting it to work. I used two lengths of pipe to get to the piece where the nipples would go.

Using a drill fitted with a 5⁄16-inch drill bit, I made three holes in the length of pipe, about 8 inches apart. Thinking this was going to be easy, I tried to pop in one of the nipples — it didn't fit. After trying for a good 15 minutes (with no success), I took the drill and very carefully moved it around in the hole, barely widening it. With this modification, some determined wiggling, and the use of a wrench, I was able to fit the nipples securely in the hole.

Fit the bucket onto the table, where you can start attaching PVC pipe.

Step 4:

I then attached the length of pipe with the nipples to the fence of my coop with cheap black zip ties. I attached the remaining length of PVC pipe, running upwards. Without an airflow, this gravity feeder won't work. The added benefit to this waterer is that it is easy to add apple cider vinegar or wormer to your flock's water.

First, drill evenly-spaced holes in the PVC pipe.

Then, fit those pesky nipples into them, however you can!

Silicone sealant is necessary for this waterer to work.

Step 5:

I thought that I was all done, but as soon as I filled the bucket with water to test my contraption, water started dripping out from all the joints. I went back to the store and got silicone sealant and then spread it around each joint to make sure it was waterproof.

Problem solved!

Conclusion

With this easy, cheap waterer (created in one hour), it is impossible for the chickens to dirty their water. My chickens weren't used to drinking from the nipples, so it took them a couple days to learn. But once I took away their other waterer, they learned to drink from this setup in a matter of hours.

The (nearly) finished waterer

EGGS

Free-range vs. factory-farm eggs

By Karen M. House

The phone rang.

"Karen?" the voice said. "This is Florence. Can I ask you something?"

Florence was my supervisor at work, a tough, hard-boiled working woman. A few days before, I had taken her a dozen of my home-raised brown eggs. This day, her voice sounded different. It had a touch of the wonder of a child ...

"These eggs you gave me, is it my imagination, or do they taste different?"

I laughed. "Well, yes, they are different," I said. "Those are fresh eggs, from chickens that eat grass and leaves and worms and bugs. Those eggs are better. They are better for you, and they have more flavor than what you buy at the grocery store."

Florence agreed. She could taste the difference!

Most people who choose to keep a flock of chickens plan on eating the eggs. While some folks raise meat birds, the primary purpose for chickens on a homestead is egg production. Statistics vary from breed to breed and from individual chicken to individual chicken, but normally a hen will start laying at about six months of age and lay 4-6 eggs a week that first season. Production slacks off a bit each season after that, and after three laying seasons, it's probably time to put the old hen in the stew pot.

Some breeds lay more than others, and some hybrids (mixed breeds) have been developed specifically for high rates of egg production. Golden Comet, Red Sex-Link, and Black Sex-Link are some of the varieties that are the best layers. As a rule, they do not "go broody" (set eggs trying to hatch them).

Besides the breed, two other factors that affect how many eggs a chicken lays are the

The color of an egg simply tells the breed of the chicken. Barred Rock, Buff Orpingtons, and Black Australorps lay eggs that are various shades of brown. Leghorns lay white eggs.

diet they are fed and the hours of daylight to which they are exposed. Some people hang a light in the chicken coop to simulate longer hours of daylight, keeping the hens laying eggs right through the winter. And most people feed their chickens a laying ration to give them the nutrition necessary for high egg production.

Eggs can be white, buff, various shades of brown ... even green or blue! The color of an egg shell has nothing to do with the value of an egg, but rather is a characteristic of the chicken that laid it. The Leghorn is a breed that originated in Tuscany, Italy, and is commonly used for commercial production of white eggs in the United States and the United Kingdom. Brown eggs tend to come from one of the heavy breeds, like the Orpingtons and Barred Rocks. And while the color of the egg has no bearing on the nutritional value or taste, some people favor brown eggs for sentimental reasons, remembering the eggs their grandmother used to raise. Others love the novelty of having pink, blue, or green eggs from Araucana or Ameraucana chickens.

In the same way, the size of the egg has very little to do with the quality of either the chicken or the egg. When heavy laying hens first start their career as egg layers, the eggs are usually small, with an occasional large double-yolk egg thrown in. Over the course of the next few weeks, the hen's eggs will grow in size until they reach what would be labeled "large" in the grocery store.

Labels

The taste and the nutritional value of an egg have to do almost exclusively with what the chicken is fed.

Unless they are labeled otherwise, the eggs for sale at the grocery store were raised on a "factory farm," where the only thing that matters is the money. Whatever brings back the greatest profit to the owner is what will be done. As a result, the chickens are crowded into close quarters in an unnatural environment and get feed that is formulated to make them produce the greatest number of eggs in their short life.

"Cage-free" means the chicken that laid the egg was not confined to a cage, but rather was free to roam at will in an enclosure, like a barn or building.

There are, however, other options — including organic, pastured poultry, and free-range. But what, exactly, do these labels mean? How are we to know the nutritional value of the egg, and the conditions under which it was produced?

In many stores, if you look closely at the labeling, you probably will see eggs from "pastured poultry," "cage-free," "organic," and "free-range," in addition to the standard factory-farm eggs. So, what's the difference?

The United States Department of Agriculture does not tightly control most egg labels, but here are some general definitions.

- **Organic.** Anything labeled USDA Organic in the grocery store has to meet certain government standards that prohibit the use of chemical fertilizers, sewage sludge, irradiation, and genetic engineering in the production of food. Eggs labeled as organic would, therefore, be expected to come from chickens fed only natural organic foods, which would mean no genetically modified organisms, or GMOs.
- **Free Range.** Any poultry product labeled Free Range has to meet certain government standards requiring that the flock must have a shelter with free access to the outdoors during their production cycle— although there is a lot of latitude as far as what "outdoors" means. It can range from

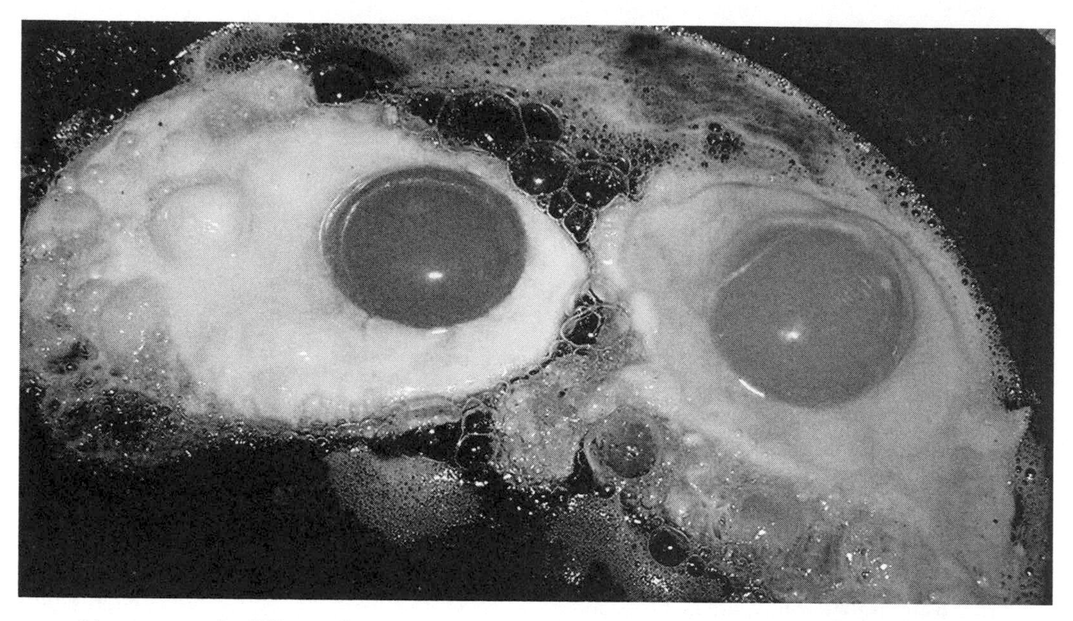

It's easy to see the difference between an egg produced in a free-ranging chicken flock eating what grows naturally in the yard (left) and an egg bought at the supermarket (right). The dark yolk means the chicken has been eating plants high in carotenoids — which protect the eyes, strengthen the immune system, and provide resistance to cancer. The firm yolk and whites of the free-range egg simply mean it's fresh.

a fenced pen to wide open spaces. They also must have continuous access to food and water.

- **Cage-Free.** This label simply means the chickens are not kept in cages. It indicates that the flock was able to roam freely in a building, room, or enclosed area with continuous access to food and water during their production cycle.
- **Natural.** As required by USDA, meat, poultry, and egg products labeled as "natural" must be minimally processed and contain no artificial ingredients.
- **Pasture-Raised.** The USDA has not developed a federal definition for pasture-raised products.
- **Humane.** Claims that animals were raised and housed "humanely" are not regulated under a single USDA definition.
- **No added hormones.** Irrelevant, since federal regulations have never permitted hormones or steroids in poultry, pork, or goat.

As you can see, some of the definitions are vague, and the government does not require much accountability. Because the USDA keeps does not keep a tight rein on egg producers' advertising and labeling, it is hard to know how the eggs you buy in the store were raised. If it says "free-range," does it mean the chickens frolicked in green, sunlit fields all day eating what's natural? Or did they live in a pen eating genetically modified (GM) grain?

There *is* a difference, nutritionally. What the chicken eats goes into the eggs that we eat.

Nutritional value

If you start investigating the nutritional value of free-range eggs compared to factory-farm eggs, right away you have a problem. You will encounter conflicting assertions, primarily because those who promote the factory farms focus on one thing, and those who promote free-range eggs look at another.

Studies done by the USDA and the egg industry in the United States show no difference in the nutritional value of the two types of eggs, but they are looking only at the strength of the egg shell and the levels of protein and fat in the egg itself. No difference there.

But studies done by other groups show a considerable difference if you look at other characteristics of the egg, such as levels of cholesterol, fatty acids, and vitamins.

The first time I realized "yard eggs" had more value than just their good taste was back in the late nineties, when I was still an active blood donor. The bloodmobile would post a report online after I donated blood — which included my cholesterol level. I had been checking it there for several years when I saw a sharp dip in the level of cholesterol in my blood.

I laughed out loud — our family of six was at that time eating 18 eggs a day from our free-ranging flock of chickens. With scrambled eggs for breakfast, deviled eggs at lunch, and cornbread with eggs in it for supper, we were consuming an average of three eggs each per day, every day. Yet my cholesterol level was the lowest it had ever been. Those beautiful fresh eggs — with the bright orange yolk that stood up in the pan and the firm whites that did not run — were healthy for me and my family!

The bright orange yolk of a free-range egg simply means the hen that laid the egg is freely eating plants that contain carotenoids — which mammals (including human beings) cannot synthesize naturally, but must obtain from their diet. Carotenoids protect the eyes, boost the immune system, and improve resistance to cancer and the effects of aging.

Yes, free-range eggs are better than factory-farm eggs.

Quality of life

God made chickens to peck the ground. He gave them long claws for scratching up small bugs and worms from under the ground. A chicken that gets to forage for its food out in the sunshine, eating what it was intended to eat, is much happier and healthier than a chicken kept in a cage on a factory farm.

Naturally-raised chickens have a better quality of life, and eggs from naturally-raised chickens add to our quality of life.

Real eggs, from chickens raised in a natural environment, taste like the eggs our grandparents ate. When I first started keeping chickens, I noticed that I quit putting salt on my eggs. The eggs had enough flavor on their own that they did not need any help.

My home-raised eggs are gathered in the afternoon and cooked the next morning. It doesn't get any fresher than that! When I buy a carton of eggs from the grocery store, I have no idea how long it's been since those eggs were laid. Sometimes, those eggs are weeks, if not months, old.

Handling fresh eggs

If an egg falls apart when I crack it into a skillet, I know it is too old. But if the egg lands in the pan looking firm, the yolk high and round and unbroken, and the egg white circled around the yolk firm and clear, I know it's fresh.

Another way to tell the age of an egg is to boil it. Old eggs peel just fine, but fresh eggs won't peel without the shell taking off a good portion of the cooked egg with it.

I only recently learned a good way to boil fresh eggs — even free-range eggs:

Bring a pot of water to a hard boil. Sprinkle some salt in the water. Then lower each egg into the water and begin timing from when the water returns to a boil. After 15 minutes, take the eggs out of the pot and submerge them in ice water. When they no longer feel warm, take them out, dry them off, and peel. They will peel just fine.

If you raise chickens, and your egg shells seem too fragile, the chickens don't have enough calcium in their diet. According to Murray McMurray Hatchery, in a year "the amount of calcium that a hen will put into her eggshells can equal 20 times the amount of calcium that is contained in her bones."

Some people supplement their chicken's diet with free-choice ground oyster shells, which you can get from wherever you purchase chicken feed. Another way to supplement is by toasting empty egg shells in the oven and crumbling them up for the chickens to eat.

Normally, washing your hens' eggs is not necessary. If they are laying in a nest full of clean hay or other bedding, the egg will be clean. When the egg comes out of the chicken, it is absolutely sanitary; it only gets dirty if it is laid in a dirty place — like the floor of the hen house.

If you don't wash your fresh eggs, they will keep without refrigeration for up to three weeks. In the refrigerator, they will keep up to six months. But this is without washing them. Fresh eggs have a protective coating that keeps them good and safe to eat for a long time. Store-bought eggs, though, should probably be refrigerated, because you don't know how old they are, and they've usually been washed.

Some people don't like to use refrigerated eggs because refrigeration changes the texture of the egg. Unrefrigerated eggs blend up easier in a recipe and make lighter, fluffier scrambled eggs. Boiled, they are not as rubbery. But, for fried eggs, use the refrigerated ones, because the yolk doesn't break as easily.

I guess the conclusion of my experience with the chicken and the egg is that fresh is *good*, and free-range is *better*. *Best of all* is raising my own hens. I know them all by name. I know what they eat and where they've been.

I improve their quality of life, and they give me wonderful eggs that improve mine.

Calcium from eggshells

By Katelynn Bond

It's a well-known fact that our bodies need calcium in order to build and maintain healthy bones and teeth, but did you know that our bodies also need calcium in order to maintain proper muscle contraction, nerve health, and cell formation? If your body doesn't get the calcium it needs from your diet, then it will start to pull calcium from your bones and teeth in an effort to balance your system, thus leading to weakened teeth and brittle bones (osteoporosis) later in life. This is especially true if you are pregnant or nursing — the "recommended" daily calcium intake for an average adult is 1,000 milligrams, but if you are pregnant or nursing that number rises to approximately 2,000 milligrams.

There are a number of different ways to meet your body's need for calcium. The first thing is to make sure that you eat a balanced diet rich in whole, nutritious foods and low in processed foods. However, that is rarely enough to get as much calcium as the body requires, so we usually need some form of supplement. Most people tend to gravitate towards a store-bought supplement. Although that is an option, calcium supplements tend to be rather expensive and the pills are the size of horse pills, which are no fun to take every day. Another option is to drink roughly two quarts of raw milk every day. For me, that doesn't work because I don't have access to farm fresh milk. The third option is to simply make your own calcium supplement from a readily accessible, easily assimilated source ... eggshells!

I first heard about using eggshells as a calcium source a number of years ago from The Bulk Herb Store (www.bulkherbstore.com) when I was researching ways to prevent bone problems. Since back problems and bone problems run in my family, I figured an ounce of prevention is worth a pound of cure. The reason for using high-quality eggshells is that they are comprised mostly out of calcium carbonate which is very similar to the calcium that is already found in our bones and teeth, making it easy for our body to absorb it. Eggshells also contain 27 microelements that our bodies need. We raise our own chickens, so I have a ready supply of eggshells at hand. It is important to use eggshells from healthy chick-

Making calcium water is quick and easy. It can be stored in a lidded container in the fridge for up to two weeks.

ens; organic is good, soy-free is better, and farm-raised is best. A good rule of thumb for determining how high the mineral content of an eggshell is: The thicker the shell, the higher the mineral content.

Preparing the shells

There are two main ways to prepare eggshells in order to use them as a supplement. The preparation for both starts the same way — with well-rinsed eggshells. I do this step as we use eggs in our daily lives; once I have an empty eggshell I run it under hot water to wash out any egg white still present (being sure to leave the membrane in place for its additional nutritional value), then lay it on a towel to dry. It is recommended that you submerge your eggshells in boiling water for 3-10 minutes in order to kill any pathogens that may be present on the shell surface, but I personally have never done that due to the fact that since I raise the chickens myself (they are a small flock) and I know everything about their health. I would recommend you boil your eggshells for safety's sake, especially if you are buying your eggs from someone else. Simply bring six cups of water (that should be sufficient for a dozen shells, adjust accordingly if you are boiling more or less) to a rolling boil and then add your eggshells. Boil continuously for a minimum of three minutes, then lay them out to dry.

What kind of climate you live in will be the deciding factor for whether or not you need an extra step in your drying process. I live in a very dry climate, so simply laying the shells out on a towel for 5-8 hours is sufficient to dry them to the brittle stage. If you live in a damper part of the world, you will need to air-dry your shells overnight and then place them on a cookie sheet to finish drying them in a 200° F oven for about 10 minutes. Regardless of what drying method you use, once your shells are dry, place them in a large Mason jar (or something similar that is relatively airtight). This will become your "bulk eggshell" container and every time you dry your eggshells, put them in this jar so they are ready for you. You will need to crush them up occasionally or else your jar will fill up very quickly. A wooden rolling pin or the handle of a stout wooden spoon works great for this because you can crush the shells directly in the jar.

Now you get to decide whether you want liquid calcium, powder calcium, or both. The recipes are as follows:

Calcium water

Use 2 Tbsp. of crushed eggshells for every 2 cups of water. Place the eggshells into a clean heat-proof glass jar, glass bowl, or glass cup and add 4 Tbsp. of lemon juice for every 2

Tbsp. of eggshells. Let sit for an hour or so (the acidity in the lemon juice helps to pull the calcium out of the shell and makes it easier for your body to use) then bring your water to a boil and pour over your eggshell/lemon mixture. Let stand until it is completely cool and then strain into a another clean glass container (this one should have a lid). A funnel lined with a coffee filter works well for straining as does a few layers of cheesecloth or tea towel placed over the mouth of a jar. When you are all done, be sure to put the lid on and label your container then store in the fridge. It should last a good two weeks. If you don't want to worry about it going bad then make your eggshell water into eggshell ice cubes! Simply fill ice cube trays with your calcium water and freeze. Once frozen, pop them out and store in a freezer bag or container for future use in drinks, soups, or smoothies. A rule of thumb for calcium water is 3-5 Tbsp. throughout the day. I usually just mix it in my tea and I can't even taste it.

Calcium powder

To make powder, just take those crushed eggshells from your bulk eggshell container, put them in a coffee grinder, and grind away. Store the powder in an airtight container and take roughly a teaspoon a day broken up into three doses or more with meals. You can mix it into a drink or food. Be sure not to take more than a teaspoon of powder a day, as too much can irritate sensitive digestive tracts. Another caution: When blending, don't use a cheap blender because the eggshells will get into/under the blade mechanism and break it. A coffee grinder or quality blender such as a Vitamix are your best bet; if you're off grid I'd suggest either a mortar and pestle or the calcium water instead.

I have to admit that of the two preparations I do prefer the calcium water as opposed to the powder. I find the water is easier to take and to make. But every person and family is different, so find what works best for you and your tribe and have at it!

Disclaimer: The statements made here have not been approved by the Food and Drug Administration. These statements are not intended to diagnose, treat, cure or prevent any disease. This notice is required by the Federal Food, Drug and Cosmetic Act.

Calcium powder can be mixed into drinks and smoothies.

What to do with an egg-bound hen

By Nell Davidsen

As I walked by my chicken coop one afternoon, I heard a strange sound coming from the nesting box. It sounded like a mix between a wail and a growl, and as soon as I heard it, I knew it wasn't anything good. When I peeked inside, I noticed Cinnamon, my Rhode Island Red hen, hunched inside one of the boxes, with her head resting on the straw.

I picked her up, and Cinnamon started making that strange noise again. I also noticed that she felt much heavier than normal.

What does egg-bound mean?

As a relatively new chicken owner, I had no idea what was going on, so I ran inside to research her symptoms on the internet. All the search results pointed to the problem: Cinnamon was egg-bound.

For those who might not know, when a hen is egg-bound, her egg is stuck in her oviduct. This is a problem most often found in young hens that have just started laying, or in older hens that simply lay really large eggs. When an egg is stuck, the hen's body will still make more eggs, which puts even more strain on her. Hens that are egg-bound for too long die from heart failure – or they die from being unable to defecate. A hen's vent is the outlet for eggs and the digestive tract.

With Cinnamon acting the way she was, I knew she didn't have much time – I had to act fast.

How I fixed it

First I isolated her from the other hens. The last thing Cinnamon needed was a curious chicken poking a beak in her nesting box.

This was the egg that blocked up everything.

With Cinnamon isolated, my next step was to lubricate her vent. Using an eyedropper, I squirted a small amount of olive oil in her vent. Some people say not to use olive oil, as it can go rancid and cause problems to the hen. Mineral oil is the recommended remedy. But since olive oil was all I had, and since Cinnamon was running out of time, I made the decision to risk it. I used only about a teaspoon of oil, and I didn't insert the eyedropper more than half an inch into the vent.

With that taken care of, I draped a towel over Cinnamon's nesting box and left her alone for about an hour. The towel provides darkness and keeps in heat, both of which help a stressed-out hen to lay. After an hour went by, I checked in on her. Sadly, she still had not laid an egg. It was time to take more extreme measures.

The next remedy I attempted was to give Cinnamon a bath. Surprisingly, chickens actually do like baths.

A year or so ago, one of my other hens was attacked by a raccoon that ripped off most of her neck. She was in bad shape, covered with mud, feathers, and blood. I needed to give her a bath in order to see the extent of the damage. To give a chicken an enjoyable bath, you need to use a container that isn't too deep. The chicken should be able to touch the bottom of the container with their feet. Fill the container with warm water to about the height of the chicken's shoulders. If you are using soap, make sure to use soap that won't strip away the chicken's necessary and natural feather oils. When putting the chicken into the water, lower them slowly and hold on tight. Once they are up to their shoulders in the water and their feet touch the bottom they relax and really do start to enjoy themselves. (The hen that the raccoon attacked healed just fine, by the way.)

Cinnamon was no exception. As soon as her feet hit that warm water, her eyes started to close and her body relaxed. Once she was in the water, I gently massaged her lower abdomen. If I massaged too hard or poked somewhere that hurt, she let me know by making that growly wailing sound. After a minute or two I got the hang of it. I massaged her for about 10 minutes, then she started pushing to get her egg out. As soon as I noticed her pushing, I dried her off with a clean towel, then put her back in the nesting box and re-covered it with the towel.

After an hour, I went out to check on Cinnamon, and there were not one but two *huge* eggs in the box. They looked like duck eggs!

These remedies worked for Cinnamon, but they might not work for every hen. I would also caution that a bath in winter might require a more thorough drying of the hen, so she doesn't freeze her tail feathers off!

Make your eggs last through winter

By Melissa Souza

If you are like most folks with backyard chickens, you probably have more eggs than you can eat during the spring and summer months. We have a large family, but we still found ourselves handing eggs off to anyone willing to take them.

Then it hit me. I needed to preserve my eggs in the same way that I preserve my produce. Although whole eggs taste the best, they do have a limited lifespan that doesn't take us through the non-laying months.

Storing fresh eggs

Farm fresh eggs can be stored unrefrigerated for about two weeks if they are unwashed. Unwashed refrigerated eggs can be kept for about three to four months. If you wash your eggs, you must refrigerate them. Washing them removes the bloom, which is an antibacterial covering that keeps air and bacteria from entering the pores of the shell. A washed egg will last about two months in the refrigerator.

When you place an egg in a carton, make sure to place them pointy side down. The air sack is in the round end, and this will help to keep moisture out of the egg. When in doubt, drop your questionable eggs into a glass of water. If they touch the bottom, they are fine. If the egg is a floater, toss it!

Although you have about a four-month lifespan on those unwashed refrigerated eggs, that may not take your family through all the winter months of no eggs.

Crack the eggs into a small container.

Freezing eggs

My favorite way to preserve eggs is to freeze them. This gives me the freshest taste.

To freeze eggs, crack them directly into small bowls or containers. You can also very gently scramble your eggs, but be careful to not add air into the mix. Then pour the mixture into the containers for freezing. Three tablespoons of the egg mix equals one egg. Scrambling the eggs allows you to add ¼ teaspoon salt per cup of egg mixture to prevent graininess. If you plan to eat the eggs scrambled, this method will result in a better texture. The frozen eggs do have a grainy texture, but adding the salt really helps with that.

Whole or scrambled eggs will keep in the freezer for about six months. To avoid bacterial growth do not thaw your eggs on the counter. Instead, move the eggs to the refrigerator the night before.

Freeze until hard.

Remove from containers and store in the freezer in an airtight plastic bag

Dehydrating eggs

Another way to preserve eggs is to dehydrate them. This is not my go-to method, because it does change the texture quite a bit. They are perfectly fine for baking, however. If you do not mind the change in texture, dried eggs are wonderful for camping or hiking because they do not require refrigeration and are very lightweight.

To dehydrate eggs, crack them into a bowl, and gently whisk. Try not to cause air bubbles. Use fruit leather trays or line your dehydrator with parchment paper. Gently pour the mixture into the trays. I find that six to eight eggs fit nicely in the fruit leather trays. The thicker it is, the longer it will take to dehydrate.

Set your dehydrator to 145° F, and dehydrate for about 12 hours. About two or three hours in, you will notice a skin forming on the top. You can break that up a bit with a fork to speed things up a bit. Once dried you can break the eggs up with your hands or blend them in your food processor for a very fine powder. Store them in an airtight container, like a Mason jar, for up to a year. To get the equivalent of one egg, add one tablespoon egg powder to one tablespoon water, and let sit five minutes. Then use as you would a raw egg.

Conclusion

Remember that both frozen eggs and powdered eggs are still a raw egg product. Wash your hands after handling both, and be sure to fully cook them before consuming.

Long-term egg storage

By Jackie Clay-Atkinson

Most of us have made the best of low egg production (or none!) all winter long. But as the days lengthen, those hens sing and begin the business of laying eggs. And suddenly, we're gifted with lots and lots of eggs… often more than we know what to do with. After all, how many fried eggs can we eat? Luckily, eggs will last for a long time if stored correctly.

Refrigerating

Eggs will store in the refrigerator a surprisingly long time. I've often had eggs in the fridge that were more than three months old that were still fine to eat. After all, store-bought eggs are often four or more weeks old when you buy them "fresh" from the store! But there are ways to make them last even longer. Eggs stored at 30° F will not freeze, but will remain good for many months. I kept eggs all winter while living at our very remote homestead up in the mountains of Montana by simply putting them on the floor of our pantry where the temps were just at freezing with no additional fuss. By spring, I did break them into a cup before using, just to make sure none had gone bad. (One way to tell a bad egg before you open it is to float it in water: Very old, bad eggs will float on the top; stale, but usable eggs will float on the bottom with the large end up; week-old eggs will float with the large end slightly

elevated; fresh eggs will sink and lie flat on the bottom.)

Waterglassing

One old method of saving eggs for many months during the winter is to use waterglass. Waterglass is sodium silicate and is often available at drugstores. You need a smaller crock with a lid or a glass gallon jar to store the eggs in. Mix the waterglass, combining 1 part waterglass to 10 parts cooled, boiled water.

Pick fresh eggs (clean, unwashed eggs store better but if you must wash, do it minimally), place them carefully in the jar, pour on the waterglass to cover the eggs by at least two inches, and cover to prevent contamination and insects from falling in. If you don't have enough fresh eggs all in one day, you can keep adding more to your container until it's as full as necessary. A gallon glass jar will hold roughly three dozen medium-sized eggs.

You should store the waterglassed eggs in a refrigerator or another cool location. Grandma stored hers in the root cellar. Waterglassed eggs will store until spring. The only problem I have with waterglass is retrieving the eggs ... I don't like having to roll up my sleeve and slide my bare arm through that solution. Yuck!

Using mineral oil

As an alternative, many people rub mineral oil all over the shells, then store them in cartons in a cool location. Just keep in mind, oiled eggs will not be able to have the whites whipped.

Freezing eggs

A popular solution to long-term egg storage is freezing them. Eggs cannot be frozen whole, or the shell will crack, so you must freeze eggs after cracking them open. You can either freeze whole eggs or separate the whites from the yolks and freeze in separate containers.

To freeze whole eggs, break into a bowl and stir just enough to mix; don't whip. If they are thoroughly mixed you won't have to add sugar or salt. Otherwise, add to each cup of eggs ½ tsp. salt (for cooking main dish eggs) or ½ Tbsp. sugar (for baking cookies, cakes, etc.). Pour mixture into smaller freezer containers or into ice cube trays to freeze individually (which makes them very handy to thaw and use later).

In order to keep whole eggs or egg yolks from becoming tough, you may add a pinch of sugar or salt. Many people freeze whole eggs or egg yolks/whites separately in ice cube trays, then when frozen, turn them out into freezer containers to keep long-term.

You can separate the whites from the yolks so you can whip the whites. But don't get any of the yolk into the white or it won't whip up. Pass the whites through a strainer, pushing with a wooden spoon to break up any thicker albumen and then freeze. To use these whites, bring them out of the freezer and let warm to room temperature before whipping them (about half an hour).

The yolks may be slightly stirred in a bowl to break them but don't whip them, adding ⅛ tsp. salt or ½ Tbsp. sugar to each four yolks to prevent them from becoming tough.

Frozen egg equivalents:

2 Tbsp. thawed egg white = 1 large fresh white
1 Tbsp. thawed yolk = 1 large fresh yolk
3 Tbsp. thawed whole egg = 1 large fresh egg

Frozen eggs will remain good in the freezer for a year.

RAISING HEALTHY POULTRY

Raising meat chickens for farmers' markets

By Allen Easterly

Chicken is by far one of the most heavily produced and commonly eaten foods in the United States. Broiler birds (chickens under 13 weeks old) account for almost all chicken production. According to the U.S. Department of Agriculture, the U.S. produced 36.9 billion pounds of chicken meat in 2010. That's a lot of birds! Only 18 percent of that meat was exported, leaving 30.3 billion pounds of chicken for consumption here in the good old USA. I'd bet my best rooster that all of the birds counted in these statistics came from commercial "chicken factories" where the birds never see the light of day and exist in crowded, filthy conditions. That's not a very good environment to grow tasty chicken meat. There is a growing movement in this country towards better-tasting, humanely-raised food, and there is a big market for free-range, pastured chicken. Selling your chickens at the local farmers' market can be highly satisfying to the customer and profitable for you. Here's how I do it.

Planning ahead

The first step needs to be selecting the breed you want to raise. There are ample resources on the internet providing short descriptions of various breeds. Most of these companies also send out paper catalogs from which you can order your chicks. Commercial growers commonly select the Rock Cornish-Cross as a meat chicken. This hybrid breed has been developed to grow fast and put on a lot of breast meat. Another plus is they have white feathers

An attractive and informative farmers' market table helps draw customers to you.

Where to pick up chicks

Meyer Hatchery
626 State Route 89
Polk, OH 44866
1-888-568-9755
www.meyerhatchery.com

Murray McMurray Hatchery
P.O. Box 458
Webster City, IA 50595
1-800-456-3280
www.mcmurrayhatchery.com

Stromberg's
P.O. Box 400
Pine River, MN 56474
1-800-720-1134
www.strombergschickens.com

Newly-arrived Cornish Rock chicks enjoy the warmth of the brooder bulbs in the corner of their 8x8-foot outbuilding box while they search the tarp for their first bites of food.

that don't leave dark "tattoo" marks in the skin when plucked. If fed properly, this chicken can provide one and a half- to two-pound Cornish hens in just four weeks, and three- to five-pound finished broilers/roasters in just seven weeks! They have an excellent feed-to-meat ratio and are available to sell at the market much sooner than other breeds. Home-raised Cornish chickens taste much better than the store-bought version when raised free-range; pasture-ranged tastes even better.

The best bargain can be had from most hatcheries by ordering chicks in groups of 100. I have found that raising 100 birds at a time seems to be very efficient for market production. The rest of this article is written with a flock of 100 birds in mind.

Before your chicks arrive in the mail, provide a large boxed-in area over a tarp in a protected barn or other outbuilding where predators can't get to your baby chicks. I bought two sheets of cheap plywood, split each sheet lengthwise and attached them to pieces of 2x2 lumber in the corners. This provides a 64-square-foot home for their first four weeks. Lay a length of 2x6 lumber over eight feet long across the top of the box down the middle and attach four brooder lamps (evenly spaced). It's a good idea to run a nail or screw in the side of the 2x6 where each lamp is attached. Attach the lamp to the board over the screw. This helps prevent the light from accidently dropping in the box and possibly starting a fire. Provide a five-gallon water jug and at least two 10-pound feeders. Have 600-700 pounds of high protein (21%) starter feed available. This should be all you'll need to feed them for the next seven weeks if you butcher half in four weeks and the rest at seven weeks of age. If you plan on growing the whole flock to full-size, you'll probably need an additional 300 pounds of feed.

Starting your chicks

It usually takes a week or so from ordering newborn chicks to delivery at your local post office. It's a good idea to call your post office and let them know you have live birds on the way. Ask them to call you as soon as they arrive. Newborn chicks can live about three days without food or water during shipment while they absorb their internal yolk sac. They will arrive hungry and thirsty. Once they arrive, you'll need to get them in your box as soon as pos-

A chicken tractor keeps your birds safe from predators while allowing ample room for exercise, fresh air, and some natural foods.

sible to keep them warm under the brooder lamps and let them begin eating and drinking. As you take each chick out of the shipping box, dip their beak in the water. They'll remember where it came from. Scatter chick starter feed on the tarp to make it easy for them to find. Most early chick deaths are the result of young birds being unable to find their food and water or becoming chilled. After about three days they will have found the food in the feeder and you won't need to scatter feed on the floor of their box anymore. This is the best time to cover the floor with wood shavings, pine needles, or other absorbent litter. Brooder lamps should be kept on continuously for the first four weeks while the chicks develop enough feathers to keep themselves warm. It is sometimes beneficial to put an additional tarp over the top of the box to help keep the heat in during cold weather. If it's too cold, the birds will huddle so tightly together that they will smother each other. This can lead to significant losses during just one cold night.

Growing tasty meat

Rock Cornish-Cross birds need to have feed and fresh water in front of them 24 hours a day. They eat almost constantly and need to in order to grow meat fast. Be sure to keep your water container and feeder full at all times. At four weeks of age, your birds will be 1½ to 2 pounds and can be processed as Cornish game hens. Many people don't realize that game hens aren't game at all, just young Cornish-Cross chickens. All the remaining birds can now be moved outdoors, preferably on pasture, in a large chicken tractor or other area where predators, including aerial ones, are fenced out. I built a 10x10-foot tractor with PVC pipe and chicken wire, with a roof half-covered with plastic roofing panels. The panels provide shade and protection from rain. Move your tractor every day or so to fresh grass and keep the water and feed coming for another three weeks. The birds will just keep getting bigger and bigger, putting on a pound or more of weight each week. Cornish birds need to be processed before they are eight weeks old. Unfortunately for them, their bodies grow so fast their heart can't keep up and they will begin dying from heart failure around eight weeks of age. So get them processed before you start losing them.

Processing and packaging for sale

When you process birds for sale, make sure you are in compliance with your state's agriculture and food safety laws. Otherwise, you may not be able to sell them at farmers' markets. Fines can be stiff! Some states have specific packaging and label requirements. Here in Virginia, the Department of Agriculture inspects your home processing facility annually and also must approve the labels you put on the package. There is an inspection fee in this state, so you might want to see how much it's going to cost where you live. Your other option is to take your birds to a state-approved processing facility. This can be costly and cuts into your profits, so shop around for the best deal.

Your bird is ready for packaging and labeling. But before you bag them up, check each bird from end to end. Make sure your bird is pretty. There should not be any tears, discoloration of the skin, bruises, or broken bones. If there are, you've just found *your* dinner; don't sell it to a customer that may be planning to serve it to guests or may think something is wrong with the bird. No one wants to buy a bird that looks like it got run over by a tractor. Check to make sure all the feathers are completely removed and no pin feathers or down remains. If you are selling them fresh, a food-grade plastic bag is adequate packaging. For those that don't sell fresh, the best way to preserve them is with a vacuum sealer. This significantly helps prevent freezer burn. If you want to stay in business selling chicken, you can't sell freezer burned meat or you'll lose that customer and maybe others as well. Regardless of the path you take, your packaging and labels should be attractive.

Make sure your packaging is durable for its intended purpose. Food-grade plastic bags for fresh chicken should not have any holes that will leak chicken juice all over your customer. Packaging for frozen chickens should be strong enough to withstand some tossing around in the home freezer. When packaging chickens with a vacuum sealer, try to keep cut bones on the interior of the package and not against the plastic, where they can poke through easily. An attractive and informative label is always a good idea. Safe handling instructions, net weight, and price should be on each label along with your name and address.

Selling at farmers' markets

Now that the birds look good, you need to look good, too. Dress for the weather in clean comfortable clothes. I've spent many a morning shivering because I underestimated the weather. You also want potential customers to feel at ease approaching you at market, so don't wear those bloodstained overalls. A neat, clean, and attractive stand or table is a big plus. A tablecloth is a nice touch. Post your prices so passersby can easily see.

Selling at markets is the easy part of your chicken hobby or business. Farmers' markets can be quite different from each other. They are all similar in what they sell, but market managers often have different rules for vendors. Shop around, visit several markets, and talk to the managers to find out if their rules are acceptable, what advertising they do, what the fee is, if they have room for you, and what your competition might be. While you're there, check the prices other vendors are getting for their chicken and try to be competitive. Pick the best market, or several markets, open on different days and set a sales goal for each market you work. A farmers' market is just like a business. The manager is the boss and the vendors are like employees. You are expected to be there on time for every market, follow market rules, and stay until the market closes. Showing up late or leaving early can result in disappointed customers and may anger other vendors and the manager. Make sure you have plenty of cash for change and accept local checks and credit cards if you can. Early in my market days, I lost a lot of sales because I didn't take credit cards. Now I do. Try to keep your prices constant so returning customers know what to expect. Being friendly and eager to answer questions goes a long way in establishing loyal customers.

Growing and selling chicken meat takes a lot of work and commitment but it can be very rewarding. You will meet a lot of interesting people, get to talk about your chickens, and hopefully make a little money in the end.

Prepare your poultry for winter

By James Kash

I don't exactly live in the wild tundra of Alaska or the foothills of the Montana Rockies. However, I can tell you that no matter where you live, a certain degree of preparation should be taken to protect your flock from colder weather and the problems that come with winter. These preparations range from increasing bedding to lighting the coop to changing your feeding practices to accommodate for a lack of natural foods available. Preparing the hens for winter is worthwhile and will definitely pay off in the long run.

Provide extra bedding

The most basic step to prepare the chickens for winter is to add plenty of extra bedding to the hen house. It increases the availability of insulation to hold heat in and keep cold out. I prefer to use straw or hay as it is much cheaper to purchase. I can use the straw in my compost heap but not the hay, since it has seeds. In addition, both straw and hay insulate better than sawdust or pine chips. As a bonus, the chickens do love to pick at any weed or grain seeds present in the bedding.

My chicken houses get completely cleaned out three to four times a year unless special circumstances call for more. Throughout the seasons I add more and more bedding as needed (this is called the deep litter method). Then, at the first of October, I clean the coop out for the last time until March of the following year. This time I scrape it out good and, if necessary, I take the water hose to it. Then, I lay the straw

in. For the first "bedding down," I use one-third to one-half bale of straw (or hay) to get the coop floor well-covered. I try to put down about six inches. I like to put lots of extra bedding in the nesting boxes since busted, frozen eggs are no fun at all. Throughout the season, I will bring in more bedding as needed, especially before exceptionally low temperatures or winter storms are predicted.

During the warm summer months I let the chickens out to free range, which provides them with lots of fresh air, plenty of exercise, and an abundance of natural food sources. However, it is not always smart or productive to let them out to free range in the winter. My main poultry house has an attached run which I use very little in the summer months since I prefer the range system. I do use the run in the winter months when good range is unavailable. With this setup I can let them out for fresh air and still keep them safe near the coop. I like to lay down plenty of straw and hay to prevent the run from becoming too muddy during the periodic thawing that takes place. This also helps add plenty of nutrient-rich mulch to the compost heap.

Cover windows (maybe)

I don't always cover my coop's windows with plastic. It depends on how many and how old the occupants are. One year I had four young ducklings in a building by themselves, and I figured they'd need all the warmth they could get, so I covered the window (and frame) with clear plastic. This is very easy to do. Just cut out a sheet of clear plastic to cover your window and frame. Staple or firmly tack the plastic into place. I had planned on covering the windows last year, but it turned out I was keeping 25 chickens, two ducks, and two geese in the hen house, and I wanted them to have extra ventilation. I didn't cover the windows, and everything still worked fine.

If you think you will need to cover your hen house windows this year, the plastic can be bought relatively cheaply at most hardware stores. This winter I will be keeping 20 young

Chickens love to dig around and search for treats in mulched yards.

chickens in the building, and will need to conserve heat for sure.

Hook up lighting for consistent egg production

The only way to get decent winter egg production is to hook up an auxiliary light source. During the winter months, as the number of daylight hours decrease, egg production will decrease, too. This is regardless of your flock's age or breed. That does not mean we can't have eggs during winter, as this is generally when we need eggs the most. As self-reliant homesteaders, we have all kinds of baking to do, plus big country breakfasts to fix.

I'm not saying you should hook up grid electric to the hen house. That is too complicated for me. I run a long, heavy-duty extension cord from the back deck, through the trees, woven into the wire of the chicken run, right through the rafters of the hen house, and hooked into the lamp. As for the lamp, I use an inexpensive brooder lamp with a regular light bulb hooked into it. I start this the first of October. You want them to get around 14 to 16 hours of light to keep egg production up. I turn my light on when I get up in the morning (around 6 a.m.). It stays on until it is daylight out. Then I turn it off, and turn it on again when it begins to get dark out. The evening turn-on time will change as the hours decrease and then increase. The lamp, regardless of normal daylight hours, will need to be turned off at around 9 p.m. By then they should have the necessary amount of light. The chickens will not lay eggs during the extra time the light is on; they will lay eggs during the normal daytime hours. The chickens will even roost at the normal time as well, and will stay roosting until the next morning. It will probably be a week or two for the light to have an impact on egg production.

Precautions will need to be taken when using these lamps. I take electrical tape and heavily wrap each connection to keep out moisture. Then I tape the cords under a surface (such as a table or porch railing) to keep them safe. I do this when connecting the lamp to the cord inside the coop as well. You will also need to keep spider webs and bedding away from the lamp in order to prevent any chance of a fire. I hang mine from a corner of the ceiling (away from the bedding) so it will light the entire coop.

Lighting does have a dual purpose. I do not heat my coop, as I believe extra bedding does the trick, unless extreme circumstances occur. The lighting will raise the inside temperature slightly and it will be 10 to 15 degrees warmer inside the coop when the light is on.

Modify feeding routines

A few changes should be made to your feeding routine in the winter to give the chickens a well-balanced diet. I like to keep the feeder and waterer in the building during winter. In the summer, I water outdoors in order to prevent messes in the coop caused by the geese. However, since it is just the chickens in the main house during the winter, I water inside. You will need to use a container that ice can be broken easily in. The inverted waterer tends not to be as effective in this situation, as the spouts can freeze up. I like to use a heavy-duty flexible tub so that I can easily bust the morning ice. If it is frozen solid, you can remove the waterer, then easily remove the ice because

A well-supplied feed room

the tub is flexible, not brittle. You can also purchase heated waterers. I have never used one, but I know plenty of folks who do.

In the wintertime, I supplement my hens' diet with a free-choice feeder full of 16% protein layer pellets, available at all times. This is not meant as the main food source. This is to fill in the gaps my other foods may not provide.

When good rangeland is unavailable, I like to provide greens for the chickens to eat. There are many options when selecting a "green feed" for the chickens. In previous years, I have sprouted grains to supply this. I have grown oats, wheat, and alfalfa as sprouted grains for green feeds. The wheat will grow and can be cut back to use several times. Eventually, it will become rootbound and will have to be sown again. The oats are usually good for one cutting, and they won't grow back well. Alfalfa, on the other hand, is slow and takes a lot longer to get growing and can't be cut back and successfully grown. I have the best results with wheat. To sprout the wheat, I take a large seed tray and fill it with good, rich potting soil. I sprinkle the seeds rather thickly over the top, take a few handfuls of soil, and then sprinkle that over the seeds. I water it well and put the tray in a warm, sunlit place. When the sprouts get about four to five inches tall, I go through with a pair of scissors and cut back the amount needed for the day's feeding. I like to do about three successive plantings to keep a good supply of greens. You can also feed the chickens any leftover greens from the garden, such as mustard, turnips, or kale. These vegetables are cold-hardy plants and will last well into colder temperatures right in the garden. You could also provide a bit of alfalfa hay for the chickens to pick at during wintertime.

On cool, crisp mornings, I throw a coffee can of high-quality game bird feed (scratch feed with about 18% protein) out in the run for them to pick at. This feed is usually seven grain and contains most of the following: wheat, oats, sorghum, millet, sunflower seeds, cracked corn, or alfalfa pellets. The feed helps create energy (through carbohydrates) to keep the birds active, not to mention it gives them a little exercise while scratching at the grains. Since it is higher protein, it will provide more resources for the chickens to use to produce those wonderful, farm-fresh eggs.

In addition to green feeds and scratch grains, I like to sort my table scraps to feed the chickens as well. Anything that is cooked generally goes to supplement the chickens or the dog. This includes cooked meat, cooked veggies, pasta, old bread, or cheese. I reserve raw foods for the compost heap or the rabbits. Feeding scraps is in debate as to whether this takes away from the dietary health of the birds. However, I feel that if given plenty of food choices, the birds will be able to choose what they need and balance their own diets. This is why I consider free-choice layer pellets a supplemental food.

Keep predators away

Predators tend to be at their hungriest during the winter months. Food sources are scarce for raccoons, foxes, opossums, and the neighborhood stray dogs. You will need to make sure the coop is secure, especially at night when some predators strike. Make sure there are no loose openings in the wire that an animal can get through. You also need to be sure the doors to your buildings are shut and secure when the chickens go to roost for the evening. I have found out the hard way that opossums come early for supper. Last winter, the door to the broiler house was open later than usual, and an opossum got in and took one of the chickens. I heard the commotion and was able to get there in time to eliminate the predator. In previous years, I have had packs of dogs come in and slaughter chickens during the daytime hours. This is probably the worst feeling of all, especially if they are a neighbor's dogs. This type of situation can get sticky. The best protocol to follow usually involves contacting the neighbor, but if they are uncooperative, the next step is calling the county pound. Generally, this will fix the problem. If not, do be warned that consequences can fall on you if you take "matters in your own hands," even though it may be necessary in some cases.

On the other hand, dogs can be used in your favor. I keep one kenneled down by our coop. The scent and the noise help keep most wild predators away. Dogs are also effective in letting you know when you have a "guest" near the hen house.

Final thoughts

If you apply these five simple tips, you can keep your flock warm, safe, and productive right through the long, cold months of winter.

Tips and tricks

for the small-scale chicken raiser

By Charles Sanders

After several years of raising chickens around our place, we learned quite a bit about them. Much of this learning was from information gathered from books and texts, from friends and neighbors, and from good old trial and error.

- When starting chicks, it is important to provide a place without corners in which the young birds might pile up and suffocate. We prevented this by starting our chicks in a child's plastic wading pool. If you use this method, be sure to get one that is at least a foot or more in depth. As the chicks grow, they can and will hop out. A deeper pool can help prevent them getting out, then chilling and dying if not discovered in time.

Nest boxes made from plastic buckets. Wooden wedges help keep straw in the nest and give the hens a place to hop onto as they enter.

- Another similar method we've used is to staple cardboard up inside the chicken house to provide the rounded area necessary to prevent the chicks from piling up. We simply cut up some large cardboard boxes and used a staple gun to attach the panels to the studs of the chicken house.

- While brooding the chicks, we've suspended two heat lamps at two different heights, and let the chicks seek out the one they want. It helps to prevent overheating or chilling of the young birds. As the young birds grow, we raised the heat lamps about an inch per week. That helps the chicks acclimate to life without heat lamps.

- New chicks like to pick at bright colors. That comes in handy when teaching them to eat from the feed trough. As you scatter the chick starter feed in the feed trough, toss in a few brightly-colored marbles. The chicks will peck at them and soon learn that the pan is the source for their feed.

- Another thing that we've found to be important is to keep fresh water available for your flock. Chickens are messy and fresh water will either need to be provided daily, or made available in a waterer that can supply water for a few days.

- Once our birds started laying, we made sure to provide a container of crushed oyster shell for the hens to pick at. The added calcium is important in the formation of their eggshells. Our homemade feeder simply had a short section partitioned off at one end where we kept the crushed shell available.

- For roost poles in the chicken house, we used long slender poles made from sassafras. The saplings grow long and straight and reportedly contain oils that help to repel mites. But wherever you live, you may use any native variety that produces long, slender saplings that can be trimmed and nailed into place. After months or years of use, the sassafras poles lose their natural oils and no longer repel mites. To help the birds out, we drizzled some oil on the poles. The birds get the oil on their feet and subsequently spread it about their plumage and skin while grooming. You might use linseed oil or even vegetable oil, if you want to.
- Hens need about 14 hours of light per day to maintain egg laying. We once experimented with adding a light on a timer to provide that amount of light over the winter. It worked well, but I would just as soon give the birds a bit of a break over the winter months.
- We made some really good nest boxes out of five-gallon plastic buckets. Placed on their side and secured to a base, the hens will seek them out for nesting. Place some straw in the bucket and help to keep it in place by cutting the bucket lid down to a crescent shape and snap it back in place. Or, you might use a piece of wood and cut a crescent shape by tracing along the inside edge of the bucket, cutting the wedge, and nailing it into place. I think the birds like the wooden wedges better as they can hop up on them as they enter the nest box.
- Although there is nothing quite like the bucolic scene of a flock of hens clucking and scratching around the farmyard, free-range chickens are frowned on or even prohibited in some areas. Many neighborhoods where chickens are now raised have rules against allowing your chickens to run free. Or, you might not like them leaving little piles on the front porch as they range about. We have found a happy medium to this potential problem by simply allowing the birds to range for only a few hours in the late afternoon. Doing so keeps problems to a minimum, but allows the birds to forage and pick up a lot of valuable, protein-rich insects and seeds. They will also peck around and get grit for their gizzard while ranging. Come dusk, they will wander right back to the hen house and you simply have to lock the gate after the last hen goes in.
- Locate your chicken house as close as is practical to your house and barn. If you locate it just an extra 25 feet further away than it needs to be, you will end up putting in about 25 extra miles of walking over a year's time. That equals about eight hours of extra effort.
- Pay attention to the shape of the eggs you get. Old-timers say you can predict the sex of the chickens which will hatch from them. Reportedly, the longer eggs will produce rooster chicks and the more rounded ones, hens.
- Finally, consider putting a capful or two of apple cider vinegar in your chickens' water. It will provide minerals which they need. Don't do this if you are using galvanized metal waterers. The acidic vinegar will work on the zinc plating of the waterer and possibly harm the birds.

I hope these tips and shortcuts help you to better enjoy your home chicken flock.

Raising organic chickens

By Allen Easterly

Raising your own birds and eggs organically can provide you with some of the highest quality meat and eggs not found in the typical grocery store. Even more satisfying is the great sense of accomplishment that comes with raising your own food from egg to dinner table and providing healthy meals for your family, knowing the ingredients are free of contaminants.

The birds are easy enough to rear that every member of the family can participate, from feeding to egg collecting, plucking, cooking, and of course eating. The organic birds and eggs you raise will taste better than store-bought, have no added hormones or steroids, and contain fewer antibiotics or other synthetic chemicals — and the birds live happier lives.

What exactly is organic?

The term organic refers to the process by which our food is raised, handled, and packaged. It does not necessarily reflect the quality of the actual chicken or egg product. It is more about the label you are allowed to put on a product you have raised for sale. The Organic Foods Production Act of 1990 requires that any chicken or egg to be sold or labeled as organic must have been raised with free access to the outdoors, fed only organic feed, and be produced and handled without the use of synthetic chemicals. This includes medications for your birds. You can't use sub-therapeutic doses of antibiotics or synthetic internal parasite controls or other medications on a routine basis. There must be an illness present before these substances can be administered. The only exception is for vaccinations. The law also requires the critters and their feed not be produced on land that has had synthetic fertilizers, herbicides, pesticides, or other substances applied within three years of harvest.

If you want to label and sell your birds or eggs as organic, the law requires that your farm be certified organic. Handling methods also

An organic, pasture-raised Cornish-Rock Cross can provide great-tasting meat in just seven weeks.

have to be certified organic. There are annual inspections and periodic testing requirements as well. The standards for certification were developed by a group of farmers, consumers, handlers, and retailers known as the National Organic Standards Board. The U.S. Department of Agriculture (USDA) provides variable degrees of certification: 100% organic, 95-100% organic, 70% or more organic, and less than 70% organic. These certification levels accommodate farmers that may have to treat sick birds on occasion. The level of certification is reflected on the product label. Another label that is related to organics but does not reflect USDA certification is Free Range. This usually means the birds were pasture-raised. Farmers using this label generally do not use growth hormones or routine antibiotics, but do not desire to have their operation certified.

Organically produced birds and eggs are usually tastier. The color is also richer. Bird skin will have a healthy yellow color instead of the pale white from a chicken factory. Organically-grown birds typically have less fat since they get more fresh air and exercise. They are also healthier since they are not confined to cramped quarters, overfed, and subjected to respiratory illnesses that are common in large chicken factory operations. The nutrient content of organic birds and eggs is generally higher because the birds have access to a wide variety of natural food items such as insects and green grasses. Organic chicken eggs will have thicker shells and the yolks will be brighter and more yellow than factory eggs. Organic eggs are higher in the amino acids important in the human diet.

Best birds for organic meat

If you want to produce organic chicken, be sure to buy feed that has been certified organic and follow the rules for application of medications. Some of the largest growing meat chicken breeds are Australorp, Buckeye, Cornish, Dorking, Java, Rhode Island Reds, Rocks, and Jersey Giants. These birds put on the most muscle and some do it faster than other breeds. The Jersey Giant is aptly named, since the cockerel (male under one year old) reaches 11 pounds in less than a year and tops out at 13 pounds when he comes of age as a rooster. His sister, the pullet (female under one year old), is quite a big girl at 8 pounds growing to 10 pounds when she becomes a full-fledged hen. Next in line is the Cornish cockerel weighing in at 8½ pounds with his plump pullet sweetheart reaching 6½ pounds. The Jersey Giants and the Cornish are slower growers so expect to put out more in feed costs for these two biggest varieties. These chickens tend to grow their bony frame first and not put on significant muscle growth until about six months old.

The Buckeye, Dorking, Java, and Rock cockerels are all about the same size, maturing at 8 pounds; however, their ladies tend to vary. The Java pullet is 6½ pounds, the Dorkings and Rocks fall in the middle at 6 pounds, and the most petite of the big girls is the Buckeye pullet at 5½ pounds.

While these are some of the biggest chickens you'll ever meet, they are not always easy to find. The most common meat chickens are the Australorp and the Rhode Island Red. The cockerel of both breeds top out at a hefty 8½ pounds. The pullets reach a plump 6½ pounds, making these two breeds good, easy-to-find choices.

These weights are at full adulthood, but they can help you determine growth speed and feed requirements. To get the best bang for your hard-earned buck, you might consider selecting a cross-breed. They usually convert food to meat more efficiently. Cross-breeds also tend to grow faster than purebred birds. A Cornish-Rock cross is an excellent example.

Organic eggs

As with organic chicken meat, if you want to your chickens to produce organic eggs, be sure to buy certified organic feed and avoid the use of any medications. Many medications will collect in the eggs and then the eggs are not safe for consumption. It can take anywhere from a day to a month for some of these substances to dissipate to safe levels in the eggs.

Information on organics

National Organic Program (NOP)
http://www.ams.usda.gov/nop/

National Organics Standards Board (NOSB)
http://www.ams.usda.gov/nosb/

Organic Foods Production Act
http://www.ams.usda.gov/AMSv1.0/getfile?dDocName=STELPRDC5060370

Organic Trade Association
http://www.ota.com/index.html

Birds given free-range or a fenced yard enjoy snacking on other delicacies such as insects, fruit, seeds, and worms. These tasty little morsels work to provide better tasting eggs and healthier birds. The birds benefit from the daily fresh greens and you benefit from the free organic fertilizer for your grass and a savings in coop cleaning labor. Chickens feeding on greens also produce eggs with richer-colored yolks.

Want more control over the color of your egg yolks? Supplement feed with wheat and barley to get light yellow yolks; yellow corn and greens produce a medium to dark yellow yolk. Marigold petals are also an excellent organic additive to the chicken's daily diet for enhancing the yolk color to a yellow-orange hue.

Organic eggs contain the highest-quality protein available and many of the amino acids essential for us human critters to build body tissues. Egg yolks are high in vitamins and minerals, including vitamin D. They are well worth the effort to start your own backyard flock.

The organic market

The USDA claims that the demand for organic products is consistently rising. Demand grows about 20 percent each year with annu-

Organic eggs are high in vitamins and minerals ... not to mention they taste pretty darn good!

al sales over $10 billion. While organic foods aren't significantly more nutritious, they lack most of the chemical and hormone substances that make their way into non-organic bird meat and eggs. This is a huge marketing advantage to our environmentally- and health-conscious public. They also realize the use of synthetic chemicals on the land is potentially harmful to our soil, air, and water supplies. The Organic Trade Association has done an excellent job of promoting organics and can take a lot of credit for educating the public on the benefits of organic farming and eating. The USDA certification program has also contributed by giving consumers confidence in organically-labeled products. Organic birds and eggs are more expensive to raise, which means they sell for higher prices than other chicken products. There are certification costs that have to be covered. Organic feed is more costly and free-range rearing methods may lead to the loss of some birds and eggs to predators. The birds also grow to market size a little bit slower since they are not overfed like factory birds. Because organically-reared birds get more exercise, it's reasonable to believe they will contain more meat than a factory bird of the same weight. The public doesn't seem to mind paying a little more for higher quality food they have confidence in, so the market should continue to climb.

Going organic can be challenging and could take some time to become certified, if that's the route you choose to take. Even if you decide to skip certification and just grow organic, the rewards are well worth the effort and extra cost. Knowing you and your family are eating the healthiest foods possible provides a great sense of satisfaction and contentment in the fact you are doing the very best you can for your family.

The chicken saga

By Karen M. House

I have raised chickens before — several times. But this time, a good friend wanted to go in together with us on a flock of laying hens. We decided to buy 20 chickens, build a hen house together, and split the cost of feed.

Acquiring chicks

Toward the end of February, I checked in at my local Tractor Supply to see when they would be getting chicks. "Next week," the lady said.

The next week, I started calling. The first day was a holiday, so there was no mail delivery. The second day, the chicks had not arrived, probably because the hatchery did not want their live cargo sitting at the post office over a long holiday weekend.

Finally, about Thursday, my call netted a positive response, and my husband and I hopped in the truck and made a run down off the mountain to check out the new arrivals.

The store had "red pullets" (Buff Orpingtons), "black pullets" (Plymouth Barred Rocks), and "black straight run chicks" (Black Australorps). Pullets are females and cockerels are males, sexed at the hatchery when they are a day old. Straight run means they have not been sexed, and you could get male or female. Straight run usually has a lot more cockerels than pullets, by the way.

Buff Orpington, Barred Rock, and Black Australorp are all considered dual-purpose poultry; they've got enough meat on them to

Two hens perch on the crossbeam of the fence. The yellow one is a Buff Orpington and the striped one is a Plymouth Barred Rock. Both breeds are considered dual-purpose chickens, raised for both meat and eggs.

eat, and they are good layers of medium to large eggs.

Since our primary purpose was a laying flock, I selected mostly pullets. But we also wanted a rooster, for two reasons: The 4 a.m. crowing is a reassuring reminder to us that we are in the country, and a rooster protects the flock.

A good rooster will lay down his life for his hens. Some years ago, I heard our roosters crowing, and noticed all the hens running for cover. When I looked out the window, I could see a hawk flying low over the yard, with the roosters all the while standing out in the open, crowing up at the invader! Another time, the two roosters in my free-range flock disappeared. The second day, when I sent my son looking for them, he found them up on the hill about a hundred yards from the hen house, torn to pieces. All the hens were alive and accounted for. The roosters (a Welsummer and a sweet little Silkie) fought the predator — probably a fox or coyote — until the hens were safely down the hill.

This time, I decided to buy nine Buff Orpington pullets, nine Barred Rock pullets, and two Black Australorp straight runs. I figured at least one of the Australorps would be a rooster.

Day-old chicks settle into their new home in the living room. A large cardboard box with newspaper for bedding provides a cozy temporary shelter.

Setting up the brooder

Home we went with our cheeping box of chicks. Until the chicks grew their feathers, they would need careful protection from the cold. In nature, they would huddle under their mother's feathers whenever they were cold or frightened, so to recreate that environment, the babies would need a close, warm place to stay until they could manage out in the hen house. That ended up being a corner in my living room.

Day-old chicks are not very big, and they needed a lot of body heat from their sisters, so a big cardboard box was plenty of room starting out. We bought a heat lamp reflector from Tractor Supply, but used a regular 40-watt light bulb instead of a heat-lamp bulb. The reflector directed all the heat and light from the bulb down into the box, and a clamp on the reflector

By the time the chicks started getting their feathers, they were growing too large for the box. We moved them into a big, old, cast-iron bathtub upstairs. We still layered newspaper down for bedding each day, and kept the heat lamp close by at one end of the tub. When the heat directly under the light was too warm, the chicks would spread out, as seen in this photo.

The hens enjoy a "salad bar" of fresh greenery picked from trees in the yard.

allowed us to mount it on the side of the box, plugging it in to the standard electrical outlet in the wall nearby.

I layered some newspaper in the bottom of the box as bedding, screwed a quart-size Mason jar of water into the red plastic waterer I got from Tractor Supply for $2 and turned it over to set in the box, screwed another Mason jar of Chick Starter feed into a tin feeder we already had, and turned it over to set in the box... and the chicks' new home was all ready for them.

I positioned the light so that it shined in one corner of the box. That way, if the chicks were too cool, they could move under the lamp, and if they were too warm, they could move away from the light to another corner of the box.

New babies went in, and soon we heard the contented rustle-and-cheep of healthy chicks in the living room.

For the next several weeks, I changed out the newspaper bedding every day, and provided clean, fresh water and feed at least once a day, sometimes more often as the babies grew. Whenever the weekly shopper appeared in my post office box, I would go dig out half a dozen that had been thrown away in the post office wastebasket. These papers provided free bedding for our chicks.

When the chicks were a couple of weeks old, I realized they were getting a bit crowded in the cardboard box, so I moved them upstairs to a big, old cast-iron bathtub. I spread newspapers, once again, for bedding. We dangled the heat lamp down from the shower-curtain rod, and the jar of food and jar of water went in the tub with them. The little balls of fluff rushed exuberantly around their larger quarters!

Every day when I changed out their bedding and refilled their food and water, I would take each chick out of the tub by hand and place her in the cardboard box. When done cleaning, I would then take each chick out of the box and replace her in the tub. This way, the chickens got used to me handling them. I knew this would pay off in the future if I needed to catch a chicken for some reason. They would not be scared or as likely to run.

Moving the chickens to the hen house

At about six weeks, the chicks were nearly full-fledged, having exchanged their fluff for feathers. That's when the hen house construction got underway in earnest. My husband and our partner in the chicken flock worked together for a couple of days, building the 8x8-foot structure with scrap lumber and bits of scrap tin for the roof. We enclosed an exercise yard with an unused chain-link dog kennel. Then we introduced the chicks to their new home.

At first, we kept the little chicken door to the exercise yard blocked, to give the chicks time to adjust to their surroundings before they roamed in the larger area. We tore two sides off the cardboard box and put the box on the floor of the hen house, right under the heat lamp so they would have a warm place to cuddle. The two remaining sides of the box were situated so as to block cold north and west winds that might find their way around the piece of tin blocking the chicken door or up through the wire floor under the roost. A long extension cord from the house gave power to the heat lamp, which was clamped to the edge of the nest boxes.

At this point, since the chicks were about six weeks old, we switched from starter feed to chicken scratch. Before we were through feeding the 50-pound sack of scratch, we had realized it was not a well-rounded source of nutrition for the birds. They did not eat all that I threw out, and they always seemed hungry. My husband talked to the people at the local farmers' co-op, and they told him to stick with the starter/grower feed until the birds started laying.

As the chicks grew, we opened the chicken door and eventually they began to venture out into the wide world of their exercise yard. And I began to feed them a more diverse diet.

Feeding the chickens

Our partner, Tom, had a larger feeder and waterer set, and I put those out in the exercise yard to feed the blossoming appetite of our growing birds. I also threw out any vegetable scraps from the kitchen in a separate spot on the ground. This included such chicken-friendly foods as leftover grits, bits of bread, and peelings from potatoes and carrots.

The third "feeding station" was the salad bar. Each morning I broke a couple of small branches off the trees and bushes in the yard, which were just starting to green up with their spring leaves, and poke the stems through the chain-link fence, where the chickens could peck the leaves off. Every few days I would pull out and discard the leafless branches.

Once the garden started coming in, I began to weed with a bucket at my side. I threw all the weeds in the bucket and when I was done, I carried the weeds to the chicken pen and threw them over the fence. Chickens are smart enough to figure out what's edible (for a chicken) and what's not.

Chicken personalities

As the chicks grew into mature-looking birds, I began to notice some of their unique characteristics. Two of the friendliest chicks were Crooked Beak and Crooked Toe. You can probably guess where they got their names!

"Big Mama" (above) turned out to be "Big Daddy." The feeder on the left is filled about halfway each day with starter/grower feed.

Crooked Beak is a big Buff that has a deformed beak that curves to one side, although from her large size and vibrant manner, I don't think it has hindered her ability to eat at all. Crooked Toe is a Barred Rock that looks as if two of his toes were broken when he was small.

A couple of the Buffs have wispy, curly feathers on their backs that look to me as if there might have been some ornamental chickens in the woodpile.

And one of the Barred Rocks always pecks me if I squat down to talk to the flock. Finally, I figured out that she just wanted attention! She will peck my hands until I pick her up and cuddle her to me. Then she makes a contented little purring sound.

The largest chicken in the lot is a Buff Orpington that's big and plump, and has bigger, brighter comb and wattles than the others. I called her "Big Mama."

At 11 weeks, I noticed the chickens' voices had changed. Instead of peeping, most of them were making the low clucking sound that grown hens make. And one week later, I heard a rooster crow.

That night the spring weather was perfect for sleeping with the window open, and I woke up to a moan out in the yard. Young roosters always sound to me as if some injured man is dying in the yard. It's a sort of ERRrrrrrr sound.

"Terry!" I said, shaking my husband by the shoulder. "Listen!"

"What?" he mumbled.

"The rooster's crowing. Listen!"

"It's just the scanner," my husband murmured as he rolled over.

"No, it's a baby rooster! Listen!"

He listened.

"Well," my husband admitted at last, "I guess we've got at least one rooster."

For a while, we didn't know which of the two Black Australorps had crowed. Then, one day when I heard the crowing, I peeked out my window to determine the source. There, proudly crowing to the heavens, was Big Mama. She wasn't a she, after all! And that fellow was getting his crow down, sounding like a real rooster!

I learned two things from that.

One I already knew: You can't tell which ones are roosters until they start crowing. The second thing I learned is those chicken-sexers don't always get it right!

The other day, I saw the two Black Australorps squaring off like they wanted to fight, so we may end up having three roosters, instead of just one. We can always put the extras in the freezer. With chickens, nothing goes to waste.

At this writing, our chickens are 14 weeks old. Thanks to a good farm dog and a good fence, we have not lost a single bird so far. Every time I feed, I count heads, just to make sure nobody's missing.

Within the next two months, we should start getting an abundant supply of wonderful tasting, farm-fresh eggs — a prize well worth the work.

Tips for raising chickens

- Start with good breeding stock. Since purebred chicks cost just a couple of bucks apiece, there is no reason to skimp on your start-up stock. Decide what you want your chickens for, and buy accordingly. A good way to start making that decision is to read through the Murray McMurray catalog or website. If all you want is something pretty to stroll around your city lot, get a few bantam pullets or an ornamental variety like the Silkie. Crowing roosters are generally unwelcome in the city, so stick with pullets. If you want something to eat insects in your yard, but are not interested in eggs or meat, get Guinea fowl. They are more independent than chickens, and are professionals at clearing a field of fleas, ticks, and other bothersome insects. And their bizarre, alien appearance is a surefire conversation-starter! For meat birds, Cornish Cross is a good breed. For egg-laying, the Black Sex-Link and Red Sex-Link can't be beat. They are a hybrid that consistently lays eggs year-round, but rarely goes broody (setting eggs to hatch them). Dual-purpose birds like the Barred Rock, Australorp, and Orpington are very common and easy to find. And if you are interested in preserving heritage breeds, heirloom varieties like Dominique and Speckled Sussex are a little more expensive, but available. Decide what you want the birds for, and only buy what you need.

- I advise against raising your own chicks from eggs, as you usually will get just one chick raised to maturity for every four or five eggs you start. The survival rate is higher for chicks hatched in an incubator than for hen-raised chicks, but an incubator is an added expense, and there is still a learning curve, during which time you likely will lose a few anyway. Getting chicks from a hatchery like Murray McMurray or Privett Hatchery — or from your local co-op or Tractor Supply — is a more practical choice for the novice chicken farmer.

- Check your chickens *daily*. Make sure they have food and clean water at all times, and count heads *daily*. A sick or injured chicken can be rescued and nursed back to health if caught in time, but sometimes all it takes is one day for it to die if you don't notice the problem.

- In my experience, heavy layers need a minimum of two square feet of housing per bird; smaller birds, less. And it is important to maintain good sanitation. Giving them plenty of room to run around outside is a good place to start. If they free-range, make sure your chickens can't get to tender young plants in the garden. They will eat the insects, of course, but they will also snip the young leaves and peck holes in your tomatoes and cantaloupes! Free-ranging gives you the happiest chickens and the healthiest (low-cholesterol) eggs, but it brings with it its own issues, such as a greater risk of predators ... and chicken poop on the porch. Second best to free-ranging would be providing a large fenced exercise yard for your flock, which will give them plenty of exercise, a few bugs and worms to eat, and a place to spread their waste around so it does not become a hazard for them and you. Do not put a board or other visual barrier across the top of your fence. If a chicken cannot see the top, it won't try to fly over. I guess they assume that fences go all the way to Heaven.

- Deworm chickens a couple of times a year with a reliable chicken wormer like Wazine (available from the farmers' co-op and Tractor Supply) or a botanical wormer of your choice.

- Egg production will begin to drop off in your hens' third year of laying, so make plans to sell or eat your three-year-old layers, and you should already be raising up a new flock. One tip to tell one flock from the next is to choose a different breed each time. That way, you can discern at a glance — the black chickens are three years old, and the red ones are a year old. Butchering a chicken you've raised yourself is a whole new level in self-sufficiency. Not only do you know this chicken, but you know it's had a happy, healthy life, you know everything it has been fed, and you know it's healthy.

And well-cared-for, home-raised chicken, by the way, is delicious!

Raise chickens for increased self-reliance, part one

By James Kash

Chickens are great livestock that can set you on the right path towards food self-sufficiency. A great homestead will almost always feature a flock of these birds. Chickens provide an abundant source of eggs, meat, and manure. They are also useful in returning profit to the homestead through the sale of eggs and baby chicks. Chickens can also be raised just about anywhere. You can find a flock of chickens in the backwoods of Montana, and you can find a small flock in the suburbs of the busiest metropolis.

It is essential to consider a few questions before starting your first flock. Why do you want chickens — do you want them for meat, eggs, or both? The next question is what level of production do you want — enough chickens to provide a few eggs for breakfast, or enough chickens to provide an abundant source of meat and eggs? These questions all need to be considered before you get started.

How I started raising chickens

I started with 12 laying hens. Then, as we desired to become more self-reliant, we increased our flock. Currently, we raise more than 40 layers, broilers, geese, ducks, and turkeys. We raise laying hens to provide all of the eggs needed for homestead cooking, and plenty to sell to offset feed costs. We also raise quite a few broilers (chickens raised especially for meat) to can and save in the pantry.

I suggest that you start small with perhaps a dozen hens for eggs. As you become more comfortable raising them, you can begin adding a few more, and maybe raise them for

Chickens are a commitment, but they are worth it!

meat. Don't take on more than you can handle; this is a hard lesson we all learn. You have to feed these birds when the snow is knee deep, water them when the hoses are frozen, and care for them when the heat is blazing. They have to be let out in the morning, and shut in at the evening. Make sure you have time to care for them.

Black Australorps are a good dual-purpose breed.

Management systems

Some folks raise chickens in a coop and run, where no outside pasture access is allowed; I don't suggest this at all for the homestead flock. The run quickly becomes muddy and mud is a safe haven for disease. I used this setup for my first flock. The run was not mulched, and water easily collected in it. I soon found myself with several sick chickens that contracted coccidiosis, a protozoan infection. This disease can kill young chickens and can only be thwarted by high-powered medicines.

The best way to raise chickens, in my opinion, is on open range. With this setup, the chickens have unlimited access to air, land, and plenty of fresh foods. The chickens are let out in the morning and shut up in the evening. There are some drawbacks: you may encounter a few predators, and your chickens will simply wreak havoc on a garden or berry patch. They will dust bathe in it and eat whatever they can find. The garden will need to be fenced off in order to keep the chickens out, or the chickens could be fenced into a large area. If you live in the suburbs, you may have to raise your chickens in a chicken tractor (a portable structure to house your flock).

It's such a good feeling to look in your nest box and see it full of freshly-laid eggs.

Housing and shelter

You should have a good shelter for your birds before you get any live chickens. It is recommended that each bird have at least four square feet inside the building and ten square feet outside of the building. An 8x8-foot chicken coop will accommodate 16 chickens if they have an outdoor run. In my experience, you can have less space per bird on the inside if you have more on the outside. Chickens will spend

Roosts are simple to make.

most of their time outside, regardless of your management system.

A good building should be well-ventilated. Chickens create tons of dust and the manure doesn't smell too good either. Your shelter should include at least one window (maybe more, depending on the size) to provide some natural lighting. The building will need to be easily cleaned out, for which reason I suggest a wooden floor. This makes it easier to clean out, and will safeguard against raccoons and opossums.

The coop should have some bedding, mainly to benefit the compost pile and to insulate during winter months. I suggest straw or hay. Some folks clean their buildings out weekly, but I find it more effective to use the deep litter method. This involves frequently adding bedding to the coop and then cleaning it out thoroughly twice a year. I find it to be cost-effective and easier to maintain.

The house should also feature an area for the chickens to roost. Chickens love to roost and are happiest when the opportunity is there. The roosts should be higher than your nest boxes. To make a roost, build a frame that looks similar to a ladder. The steps of the ladder can be made from smaller tree limbs or cut lumber.

You'll need nesting boxes in your coop as well. This will be where the hens lay their eggs every day. The boxes need to be around 14 inches wide, deep, and tall to provide adequate room for nesting. You need a minimum of three nesting boxes in your coop, and should have additional box for every five birds. The boxes also need to be about two feet off of the floor to encourage your birds to use them. I suggest you build them in a cubicle-like style, as this will ensure the hens can't roost on them.

These chicks are happy and warm.

Pickin' your chicken

I prefer old-fashioned, dual-purpose breeds as the main members of my flock, such as Buff Orpingtons, Black Australorps, Dominiques, Barred Plymouth Rocks, White Plymouth Rocks, and Rhode Island Reds. They lay a good amount of eggs, forage well, and sometimes have the inclination to hatch their own young. After they have passed their prime, they are large enough to eat. However, I do like a little variety to my flock. I also have a few White Leghorns, Easter Eggers, and Silver Laced Cochins. The dual-purpose breeds all lay big brown eggs, but the White Leghorns lay white eggs and the Easter Eggers lay blue or green eggs. I have Cochins in my flock because they often go broody, which is critical for a self-reliant flock. Combined, these breeds make up a great chicken flock.

If you are interested in raising chickens for meat, there is no competition — in terms of feed-to-meat ratio, the Cornish Rocks are the best. They are ready for slaughter in six to eight weeks without any hormones or growth supplements.

The most important thing to do is thoroughly research each breed before you purchase it. I look for egg-laying ability, forage ability, size, broodiness, and the breed's overall health. Some breeds possess most of these characteristics and some possess one or two. However, when combined they will make a great flock.

Acquiring chickens

You can acquire your first "feathered friends" a few different ways. You can buy adults that are currently laying. Use caution, because sometimes you will end up with somebody's

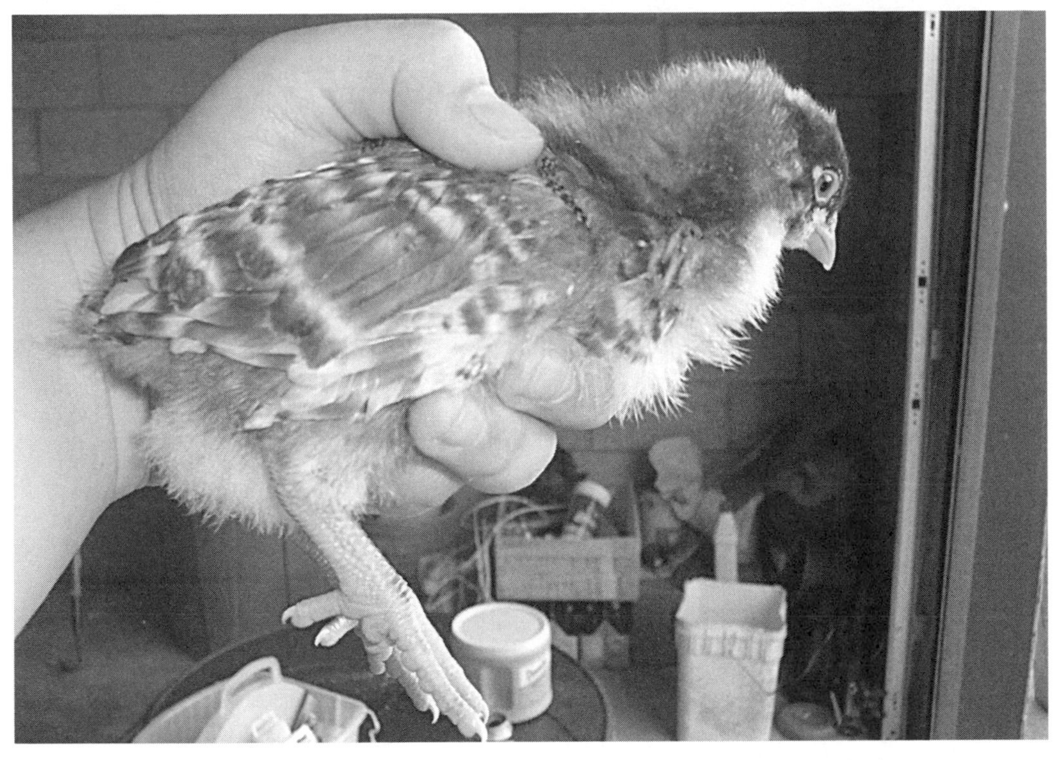

This chick is just about feathered out, and is ready to move out of the brooder box.

duds. Adult birds can be found by looking through Craigslist. You may also call around your community and look at the advertisement section of your local feed store. Using this method, you can also acquire 16-week-old pullets (young chickens that haven't laid an egg yet).

I prefer to raise chickens from chicks. That way, you can know that they were raised well and fed right. You can be more selective about your varieties. Chicks can be acquired a few ways. They can be bought from local breeders and feed stores, hatched from eggs at home, or delivered by mail order. In my area, the most economical way is to buy chicks from mail order hatcheries.

Raising baby chicks

Chicks are one of the most hardy baby livestock to raise. Regardless of how you obtain your chicks, there are few things that need to be taken care of ahead of time. You need a brooder — an area where chicks are raised. A brooder can be made from metal or hard plastic water troughs, scrap lumber, a spare cage, or even an old box. I prefer using a cardboard box. It is much easier to dispose of, not to mention you can usually dumpster dive and get a free one. The brooder needs to be solid and draft-free. Your brooder should be a comfortable size for the chicks, around eight square feet for a batch of 25. The brooder should have pine shavings or hay bedding. I like to use hay, as the compost is much nicer with it. They also can't kick it into their feeders or waterers like they tend to do with pine shavings.

You will need a suitable place to put the brooder as well. Chicks can create a lot of dust and smell if the brooder is not cleaned out every few days. They can be kept in the garage or basement, and maybe in an outside building that is secure.

If you ordered from a hatchery, your baby chicks will arrive and will not have had any food or water while being shipped, as the yolk of their egg provides them with nourishment for 3 to 4 days. Your brooder will need to be ready when they arrive. The bedding should, for the first three days, be covered with paper towels as this will encourage them to eat feed instead of shavings or pine dust. You can make chick feed or pick it up from your feed store, where you can buy a screw-on feeder or a trough-like feeder. I feed my chicks non-medicated 20% protein feed.

The chicks should also have water available. Many hatcheries will encourage you to purchase electrolytes to mix in their water for when they arrive, but I don't regularly do this. If the chicks are "dull" when you get them, I suggest you mix a tablespoon or two of sugar into their water to perk them up. As you remove each chick from the box, be sure to dip their beak into the water so they will know where it is.

Provide a heat source to keep the babies warm. I use regular heating lamps with 250-watt red heat bulbs. For the first few weeks, the lamp will need to hang about 20 inches off the floor in the middle of the brooder. As they grow and feather out you can raise the lamp higher until they no longer need it.

Brooder to eggs

Depending on your chicks and climate, the brooding stage lasts around four weeks. I have had some batches of chicks that feathered out in no time at all and others that seemed they would never grow.

After the brooder stage, you have an interim period before eggs begin to appear. During this time, chicks will grow and feather out. Move your chicks out of the brooder when they are feathered out well. Then, move them into their coop. You will need to lock them in their building for two weeks to ensure they learn where home is. This is absolutely essential. They will learn the places to roost and nest, and will return to the coop every evening.

During this stage, I continue feeding a 20% protein feed, and I also let them begin to free range and eat kitchen scraps. They will need to have plenty of water handy. Your chicks will soon begin to look and act like adults.

At around 16 to 24 weeks of age, the hens' combs will get larger and redder. The hens will begin to look heavier, and will act more like adults. Soon young roosters will have their tail feathers, and will begin mating with the hens (which is not essential for egg production). When these signs begin to occur, your first "hen berry" will be right around the corner.

Getting your flock off to a good start is crucial. In part two of this article, we will look at how to take care of an egg-laying flock from feeding to predators and pests.

Raise your own chickens for increased self-reliance, part two

By James Kash

In the first part of this series, I discussed how to improve your self-reliance by raising a flock of chickens. I explored different aspects of raising them, including their housing requirements, feeding guidelines, and basic brooder setup. We also looked at different chicken breeds and their place in a self-reliant flock.

In part two, we will look at basic day-to-day care for adult chickens, including feeding and watering, disease management, predators and pests, behaviors and productivity, and mixed flocks.

Feeding and watering your adult flock

Many experts will tell you that the only way to ensure excellent productivity is to feed your birds a diet entirely made up of 16% protein layer feed. While I recognize that free-ranging won't provide a complete diet, I do not think we should be providing our flock with just one type of food. The poultry flock will benefit from variety in their diet, and it will also be easier on your wallet.

Bagged feed should not be the primary ration available to your flock. I equate it to humans consistently eating fast food and never anything else. I encourage everyone (if possible)

My black sex-link hen is picking through the grass and clover. Chickens will pick for seeds and bugs, which they use to make those big, beautiful eggs.

My homemade feed mix is a blend of whole oats, black oil sunflower seeds, whole corn, and 20% protein laying pellets.

Water is an important resource for every living thing. These hens are taking a drink from the stream that flows by my coop.

My veterinary bag helps me with most basic infections and injuries. I encourage all poultry owners to have one.

to allow their birds to free-range. Free-ranging chickens get plenty of air, exercise, and natural food choices.

In addition to these feed choices, your chickens should also reap the harvest in much the same way that you do. My chickens love it when canning time comes. They get to pick at buckets full of tomato scraps, corn cobs, and many other vegetable scraps. If I have any pumpkins or squash that aren't prime for storage, I throw them to the flock. Of course we all find those way-too-huge cucumbers every now and then. Chickens love those as well. I actually had one of our friends lay back those missed cucumbers to feed to the flock.

I make sure to give them any meal scraps that can't be used anymore. I also throw them any bones left from meat canning, which gives them a good source of protein. Many folks mistakenly believe that chickens should be given vegetarian diets. The truth is, chickens are omnivores and will eat plenty of grubs and bugs.

You can also feed your flock sprouted grains. I like to do this during the winter when greens are not available. I sprout oats, wheat, and alfalfa. Take four trays, fill with black potting soil, and place in a well-lit place (usually in the basement window). Sow the grain seeds and lightly cover with potting soil. Keep the soil moist to allow it to sprout. It should sprout in the first few days. Begin to harvest when the sprouts are about four inches tall; simply clip with scissors. I prefer to sprout wheat as it will grow back three or four times before becoming too mature to use. I could only successfully get one cutting from oats and alfalfa. You can sow each tray in succession to keep a steady supply of green feeds.

Laying hens will also need to have a free-choice oyster shell supplement (Caution: The dust is highly toxic, so wear gloves and protective facial covering) to provide calcium. You can also give them egg shells if you desire. Grit may be necessary if they do not have ample outdoor access where they can pick up gravel and other small rocks. Grit is necessary to grind up their food.

Chickens also need to have an adequate supply of fresh water. I keep a five-gallon water fount full at all times to water the chickens. The fount is not big enough for the duck or geese to muck up, so it stays clean and drinkable far longer than regular tubs.

Disease, injury prevention, and management

Poultry are some of the hardiest critters around. If you do your best to take care of them, you will have minimal problems.

If a chicken gets a disease it is usually due to two reasons: it wasn't fed well enough or despite the good nutrition, the environment overwhelmed the chicken. Proper nutrition and housing will go very far in disease prevention.

Your building needs to be well-ventilated and cleaned regularly. The dust and mud (if in a small run) will breed bad health faster than a fertile rabbit.

In order to prevent disease and injury, you need to watch your birds. Healthy chickens will be physically active with a healthy appetite. Their combs will be big and bright red and their feathers will be shiny (unless they are molting). Legs and feet will be free from parasites. They won't sneeze or make any unusual sounds, and they'll be at a good weight for their breed. Sick chickens will be hunched over and huddled up like they are cold. Their combs will be pale and slightly smaller. The feathers will be dull and their eyes will blink continually like they are dozing off. Chicken feces will also tell a lot about their health; some runny stool is normal, but most should be solid and it should never be bloody.

In my experience with chickens I have only ever had one major, devastating health crisis: coccidiosis. This is a protozoan infection that takes place in the intestines of the bird. It usually occurs in young chickens (6 to 18 weeks of age) and can be devastating. I lost 75% of my first flock due to this infection; however, that was due to my negligence. I did not feed them correctly nor did I practice the best sanitation habits. I also used rotted sawdust as my bedding in the coop which could have held the spores. Therefore, I paid the cost for it. Most things are preventable.

I keep a basic veterinary bag on hand that will manage most general problems. My vet kit consists of antibiotic ointment, gauze and tape, iodine, petroleum jelly, powdered amprolium (commonly called Corid for coccidiosis infections), electrolytes, sulfa meds for extreme coccidiosis cases, Duramycin, and oxytetracycline. My philosophy with the chickens has always been if this basic set of supplies couldn't fix them, then I would cull the animal. This rarely happens as they are very hardy. Some may see this as callous and cold-hearted, but chickens are not irreplaceable: they are easily acquired and easy to care for.

If you have a bird with a physical injury they are usually very easy to work with. Restrain the chicken and remove any debris from the wound. If necessary, cut away part of the feather. Clean the wound well with antibiotic soap, and then clean with iodine to kill any bacteria. Apply your antibiotic ointment and bandage it up. After dressing the wound, isolate the chicken from the other birds to monitor and care for it. Recently, one of my Easter Egger pullets got in our German Shepherd's kennel and the dog wasn't very merciful. It had also just rained so the hen was very muddy. My sister, Hannah, found her and she was unrecognizable. I had almost given up hope on her — she looked awful, but I gave her a chance as she was nearing production. I took some dish soap and bathed her, then dried her off well. I cleaned the wounds and somehow she made it! Wounds are a lot easier to clear up than disease in my experience.

Predators and pests

When it comes to predators, chickens are always the prey. Regardless of where you are, you are bound to have some animal lurking around that would just love to get one of your hens. Each predator is different, but to defeat them you must first understand them.

Most predators will strike at night. The neighborhood opossum, raccoon, and weasel will

Roosting is a natural behavior for chickens and turkeys. Industrial agriculture prohibits poultry from exercising basic behaviors.

all strike after your hens are on the roost. This makes building a secure chicken coop a must, and shutting the door after they have gone to roost is also essential. Any holes need to be patched up; if a raccoon can get its nose through the hole, then it can enter the building. If you are late closing your chickens in for the night, you are giving predators plenty of time to get in. In most circumstances, these predators will take only one bird each visit. Predators are also more prone to strike in the wintertime when there are not ample food supplies around.

Stray dogs make opossums and raccoons look innocent — a stray dog will destroy a flock. The worst part about them is that they strike during the day, in most cases. Stray dogs usually do not kill for food, but for sport. About four years ago some neighbors left their dogs to fend for themselves and they eventually visited my free-ranging chicken flock about half a mile away. In order for chickens to have plenty of room to range and exercise you have to have a pretty big place, and we decided early on that we would take the good with the bad while allowing them unlimited outdoor access. This was just one of the prices that we paid. The dogs killed about eight chickens. They also ripped the bottom out of two rabbit cages and killed two of my rabbits.

Chicken hawks can also be nuisance for your smaller birds. The easiest way to protect your flocks from aerial threats to provide good cover for them, whether it is under a tree or on top of the coop itself. We have plenty of hawks in my area, but I've only lost one or two chickens to hawks in past years. It's my opinion that my geese scare away the hawks, as they are so loud and obnoxious.

Be very cautious and pay close attention to your environment for signs of these critters, whether it is tracks or scat. You can take a few preventative measures even if your flock is not enclosed during the day. We have two dogs kept around the homestead to help prevent predator problems with the poultry flock or the vegetable garden. They seem to do a good job, and are worth occasional problems.

Your chickens can also be bothered by microscopic pests such as mites, lice, and worms. My treatments and preventions are minimal; some say that a certain chemical/nutrient in winter squash seeds will rid organisms of internal parasites. I don't know if that is scientifically accurate, but it works for us. Each year I grow plenty of extra squash and occasionally give the flock some to eat and pick clean.

External parasites can be fairly easily detected by simply inspecting the feathers of a chicken. They should be clean from small larvae and eggs. The feet should also be clean. Scaly leg mites are the easiest to detect as they will form large, bumpy callouses on chickens' legs. You can fight them by coating the affected bird's leg in petroleum jelly. You can also lightly dust each bird in a powdered pesticide like Sevin dust. Cedar shavings are also supposed to repel insects so bedding your nests with them can be a smart idea.

Behaviors and productivity

Another key to a successful chicken flock is to understand your birds and know how you can help them along the way. Brooding is a natural behavior that hens go through. This is when a chicken decides to sit on eggs and hatch them. It is most commonly seen in traditional dual-purpose breeds, having been bred out of most other breeds so as not to interfere with production. A broody chicken will be very protective over a particular nest in the coop. She will look very puffy as she uses her mass of feathers to keep the eggs warm. A few times during the day she will turn the eggs, and will then settle right back down. She will sit on anyone's eggs underneath her regardless of when they were laid.

The only way to have a successful broody hen is to isolate her from the rest of the flock. If she broods in the regular boxes, fresh eggs will be laid daily in her nest even with her there on it. I have cages to isolate broody hens. They don't have to be big — maybe 18x18 inches. You will need to allow room for a nest box and a place for water and feed. The incubation time for chickens is approximately 21 days, and during the third week you should provide non-medicated chick feed. Chick feed is higher in protein, which she will need to remain healthy.

After you have spotted your broody hen, give her a couple of days in the normal nest to make sure she is serious about being a mom. Some

A broody Australorp hen in her nest box, which is in a cage in the coop. She is sitting on 10 eggs.

This chicken is recovering from this year's molting process.

other signs is that she will cluck in a grumpy tone, and will be very protective over her spot. If she is still there after a couple days, you can move her at night to her brooding home. You'll want to discard any eggs she has been sitting on — they were all laid on a different date, which will make chaos for hatch day. You'll want to give her 8 to 12 big eggs that are free from cracks, dried-on-egg yolk, and manure. Slip them under the hen after she settles into her box.

Hatch day will occur about 21 days after the first day of sitting on the new eggs. I prefer to let the hen raise the chicks if possible, as I believe it gets them off to a good start. You'll want to keep them separated from the main flock for 4 to 6 weeks to ensure the safety of the chicks.

This will bring in home-hatched babies from your own flock. Hens can brood at any time of the year, but most will usually brood in early fall and mid-spring.

Molting is a natural process that every chicken will go through, regardless of sex and breed. It is simply the shedding of old feathers and the growing of new ones. Egg production will go down during this time, as more energy is focused toward a new growth of feathers for winter. This will happen in late summer and early fall. Feathers are made mostly of protein so you may need to add a little more protein to their diet during that time.

Chickens need dust baths to clean themselves (it's equivalent to us taking a shower), and these baths also play a role in establishing pecking order in the flock. You'll need to make sure they have a place to do this, whether it is a pile of sand near the coop or a dirt patch.

In addition to dust bathing, chickens love to scratch in loose substances like straw and soil. Chickens will scratch out a flower bed faster than anything I know of. They will also destroy a vegetable garden. Chickens should be fenced out of anything like that you do not want destroyed.

Once chickens begin to lay, production will steadily rise. Most breeds lay about 3 or 4 eggs per week. However, some breeds, such as the Leghorn or Red Star, lay around 5 or 6 eggs per week. A hen will have a high level of egg production from the time she starts laying until she is about two years old. After that, she will gradually decrease production.

During her period of production she will slacken off during cold weather as the amount of daylight is less, and hens have to have around 12 hours of light for consistent egg production. Despite popular belief, you do

This is my youngest and most handsome rooster. Roosters play a pivotal part in finding food and defending the flock.

not need a rooster to have eggs. However, you will need a rooster if you want fertilized eggs (there is no difference in taste between the fertilized and unfertilized eggs). Roosters love to crow and will do so all day long, not just in the morning. I like to have roosters around because they are essential to having a good flock. Having a rooster means you can reproduce the chickens within the homestead, and the rooster plays a pivotal role in leading the flock. Roosters will softly cluck for the hens when they find food and will protect their girls, regardless of the threat.

Mixed poultry flocks

You'll find that many homesteaders raise more birds than just chickens. A homestead flock full of chickens, turkeys, ducks, and geese is entirely possible if you will follow a few simple tasks.

Chickens can transfer a disease commonly called blackhead disease to turkeys. I have never had a turkey with blackhead disease, nor have any other homesteaders that I know. Blackhead is usually found in the soil and is picked up by chickens and passed to turkeys. It has no ill effects on chickens, but can be devastating to turkeys, so keep this in mind if you have a mixed flock.

The males of each species will try and dominate each other, and it is possible that some damages may occur. Usually after some time, they will settle into a pecking order. However, if they are raised on a free-range setup you can usually avoid these conflicts as they are separated and have plenty of room to roam. You do have to worry sometimes about a tom turkey attempting to mate with a hen, as that will usually harm the hen.

In a closed system, I would not raise waterfowl with my turkeys and chickens. Ducks and geese are extremely messy with their water, and wet conditions breed disease. However, with my free-range system, this is not a problem.

A word of caution about geese: They can be aggressive with other fowl. I don't recommend geese sharing houses with other birds. I have had one instance of a goose hurting another bird, and it wasn't a good experience. However, I don't think my homestead would be complete without my pair of geese — they play an important role in keeping everyone safe. They are great watchdogs, and will attack or scare any foreign intruder whether it has four legs or two. So just give them their own housing.

I have had great luck with mixed flocks. I find them to be useful and interesting to watch and observe. A mixed poultry flock can also vary your source of meat and eggs, which can play an important role in increasing your self-reliance.

In the next and final part of this series, we will take a look at caring for your eggs, selling eggs, making money, and cooking or canning chicken.

Raise your own chickens for increased self-reliance, part three

By James Kash

In part two of this series, we discussed how to properly maintain and care for a chicken flock. This final article will explore the process of caring for your eggs, using your chickens'meat, and making a little profit along the way — all of which contribute to the self-reliant homestead.

Collecting and washing eggs for eating

I prefer to collect my eggs once a day in the evening. This ensures that all of the ladies have had the chance to lay their eggs, and none will get left overnight. I have found that eggs left overnight have an increased chance of getting manure on them or breaking.

While on the subject of eggs, you do not need a rooster to have eggs. The hens will lay whether he is there or not. However, if you intend to hatch chicks or sell hatching eggs, you will need to have a rooster for fertilized eggs. I have always had a rooster around. They are funny to watch, and play a big role in the pecking order.

You can buy cleaning solutions for your eggs. However, in the spirit of frugality and common sense, we rinse our dirty eggs in water and dry them off with cloth rags. We throw out any that have cracks or nicks in the shell. If there is a patch of manure that is stubborn and will not come off, we use baking soda to get it off the shell. Once eggs are washed, they need to be refrigerated.

Collecting and handling eggs for hatching

Hatching eggs and eating eggs all come from the same animal, but you have to do things a little differently. First, you must have a rooster in the flock to fertilize the eggs. No rooster

means no chicks. A common misconception is that a rooster will only breed hens of his breed. This is false. In order to have purebred hatching eggs, you will need to isolate the breed from the others and wait six weeks to make sure that any fertilization is by the new rooster. Hens can store sperm from other roosters for up to a month or more. On my homestead, I usually just hatch my mixed-breed hens. The blending of traits gives us hybrid vigor which is good for health and production.

I am very particular about my hatching eggs. The eggs need to be naturally clean: no manure and no egg yolks on the shell. Hatching eggs cannot be cleaned as described earlier. Washing the egg removes the antibacterial layer and will expose the developing embryo to diseases. If I am collecting eggs to hatch, I like to collect eggs multiple times a day to keep them clean and to keep extreme temperatures from hurting the egg. Intense cold or heat can affect hatch rates. You can keep these eggs for up to four days before incubating them. This will allow you to be able to collect a larger number before beginning to incubate.

A basic introduction to egg incubation

I have incubated eggs many times, and several factors influence the hatch rate.

Incubation of chicken eggs takes about 21 days. Eggs will also need to be turned during incubation, which can be accomplished by hand turning or a mechanical turner. I much prefer the mechanical turner. The temperature must be kept steady at about 100° F during the entire 21-day process. The humidity will need to be around 55% for the first 18 days of incubation. The last three days of incubation, humidity will need to be elevated to around 75%. To do this, close all the air vents and add extra moisture. You will find it essential to have a hygrometer and thermometer in your incubator to monitor the conditions. Basic operation of the incubator differs depending on what type of incubator you own. Some operate with fans, and some operate without them. Be

sure to read your instruction manual, as incubation can be tricky.

During my first try, I incubated 12 eggs and only had one hatch. The temperature spiked on the final day, drying up the shell and membrane, which kept them trapped in. Thus, they died. It is a very delicate process, but you cannot assist them in hatching out. It never works. They will not live or function correctly. They have hatch out themselves. The chick that did hatch lived only because she was about four hours early and I removed her once she was dry. She became known as "Whodat" and lived in a box in my room because we didn't want her to be lonely.

Trying to break even or make a profit with your flock

When I started our homestead flock, I knew that we weren't going to get rich. We started it so that we could further our own self-reliance and independence. Making a decent living from poultry production can be challenging, and on the self-reliant homestead we shoot to break even and maybe make a little profit.

The first step in making sure you at least break even is to reduce start-up and operating costs. This could be accomplished many different ways. Renovate an old outbuilding for a poultry house or build one using recycled materials. Anything you can do to cut startup costs will save you big bucks along the way. Feed will be the number one cost you will encounter. As discussed in the last installment, feeding should be integrated, allowing for free range, scraps, sprouted grains, etc. Just recently I have discovered a new source of feed that is saving me almost $10 to $15 a month. I used to feed Purina Layena pellets, but they cost us around $16 for a 50-pound bag. I have since found a new feed that is milled locally and is only $11 for a 50-pound bag. Cutting operating costs is the only way to save money.

The only way to make profit is to identify a market in your area. Folks are becoming increasingly more inquisitive about their food. I would much rather pay more for a product if I personally knew the person who raised it. Use these techniques to bring a little profit to your homestead. You can sell fresh eggs to eat for around $2 a dozen in my area. However, you can probably get a little bit more if you live near an urban or suburban area where demand for local foods is high. Egg sales can potentially allow you to pay for your feed and supply costs, but I have found any real profit is in hatching eggs and chicks.

Hatching eggs for purebred chickens can bring quite the price if you have good stock. I have sold hatching eggs from my mixed breed biddies for around $8 a dozen before, which is four times the profit you make selling eggs to eat. If you do raise purebred chickens to sell hatching eggs, your best outlet will be found online. You may also consider trying to sell your hatching eggs on websites like eBay or BackyardChickens.com, a specialized website for chicken enthusiasts. I have had the best luck selling baby chickens. I usually hatch them in my incubator, and keep them in my brooder until someone buys them for $2 a chick if they are under two weeks old. Then I add a dollar for every week after that until they are around laying age. The trick is to sell the chicks when they are young to keep feed costs down and to move your male chicks before gender can be determined.

Advertisement is the key to the success of any operation wanting to sell their product. You can use Facebook to advertise your eggs and chicks locally, as well as run an ad in your local paper. I also put notices up at feed stores and grocery stores to let folks know I am selling eggs and chicks. You should encourage your customers to tell their friends what you are selling. Word-of-mouth advertisement will help sell your product effectively, too.

Chicken in the kitchen and pantry

Another way to help break even with raising chickens is to eat them for meat. Chicken is very versatile. Your home-raised chicken meat and eggs will give you immense satisfaction, and they are much cheaper than buying them at the store! Listed below are recipes to use your home-raised chicken should you decide to slaughter any birds. Happy canning and cooking!

Canning deboned chicken

This is one of the best canned items I've made so far. Deboned chicken is handy in many meals. When canning deboned chicken, I can both the dark meat and the white meat. Breast meat is my favorite to can as it tastes so good.

To can deboned chicken, you need to boil the meat until the outer part is cooked. I cook white meat and dark meat in different pots to keep them separate. Remove the meat from the bones. Fill the hot, clean jars with the meat and cover with leftover cooking liquid. Place jars in the pressure canner and process (based on manufacturer's instructions and your altitude) for 75 minutes for pints and 90 minutes for quarts. I can our chicken in pints *and* quarts to give us variety for different recipes.

Canning chicken broth

Broth is easy to make. After you have deboned your chicken and packed jars to can your meat, you can begin to make broth. Simply take leftover bones and cooking liquid, and place in a large pot. Fill the pot with water and start seasoning the mix. I usually add two or three bay leaves, onion powder, salt, and black pepper to taste. You may also cook some onions or celery in the broth if you wish for added flavor. Cook this mix until your desired flavor is met. This may take anywhere from two hours or until the next day. It gets richer the longer it cooks. When the broth meets your taste requirements, skim off any foam, fat, or meat debris. Then fill hot jars with the hot broth. I usually place a wire strainer basket over the jar funnel to catch any bits of meat, small bones, etc. Leaving one-inch headspace, place previously-simmered lids on the jar and gently tighten a ring onto the jars. Place filled jars into your pressure canner, and process according to your manufacturer's instructions. Quarts need to be canned at your appropriate pressure for 25 minutes, and pints for 20 minutes. I suggest canning broths in a variety of both pints and quarts. This broth is great in many meals; it forms the base of dishes like chicken stew, chicken noodle soup, chicken and dumplings, and can add flavoring to a number of dishes.

Chicken casserole #1

1 quart deboned chicken or 4 cups cooked chicken
1 cup celery, finely chopped
1 cup fresh mushrooms, chopped (optional)
1 can cream of mushroom soup
1 can cream of chicken soup
bread crumbs, French-fried onions, or any other topping

In a medium pan, add one quart of diced chicken with the liquid included. Next add celery and mushrooms. Now pour in cream of chicken and cream of mushroom soup. Mix well. Gently heat until warm in a casserole dish, then top with seasoned bread crumbs, French-fried onions, or any other topping. Bake for 30 minutes at 350° F.

Chicken casserole #2 (my favorite)

1 stick butter
1 can evaporated milk
1 can cream of mushroom soup
1 quart deboned chicken or 4 cups cooked chicken
buttered bread crumbs

In a medium saucepan, melt butter. Then add the milk and soup. Slowly heat, and blend until smooth. Place chicken in a medium casserole dish, and cover with sauce, making sure to blend it well. Top with buttered bread crumbs and bake for 30 minutes at 350° F.

Quick chicken noodle soup

2 quarts chicken broth
1 pint chicken breast pieces or 2 cups cooked chicken
1 pint carrots, diced
1½ pint celery, diced
2 cups egg noodles
salt and black pepper, to taste

In a medium pot, pour in chicken broth and add chicken and vegetables. Stir together and add egg noodles. Heat for at least 15 minutes or until noodles are tender, then salt and black pepper to taste. You may want to add some rosemary leaves or crushed sage to it as well. It will give it a nice taste. This makes "from scratch" soup a piece of cake.

Chicken pot pie

Filling:
½ cup butter
½ cup flour
1 quart chicken broth
¼ cup milk
1 pint deboned chicken (preferably white meat)
1 pint carrots, diced
1 pint corn
2 cups pre-cooked cubed potatoes
1 cup peas (frozen, preferably)

Biscuit crust:
4 cups flour
3 tsp. baking powder
1 tsp. salt
2 Tbsp. sugar
1½ cups milk (or buttermilk)
½ cup butter (melted)

In a medium pot, melt the butter. When fully melted, whisk in the flour. Once smooth, stir in a quart of chicken stock. Stirring occasionally, let this thicken on low heat. You will want this fairly thick; when desired thickness is reached, add milk and stir well. Add in chicken and vegetables. Mix well, and keep warm over medium heat.

For the crust, mix all dry ingredients in a large mixing bowl. Smooth out a "crater" in the center and add the milk and melted butter. Take a spoon and work the dough together until smooth. Pour out dough on a floured surface and work well. Roll out biscuit dough to be fairly thin. Grease the sides and bottom of a 9x13-inch casserole dish. Place dough to cover bottom and sides. Pour in filling (you will have quite a bit left) and leave about three quarters of an inch between the surface of the filling and the rim of the dish. Now with the remaining dough fix a top crust for it. Bake at 450° F for 15-20 minutes. The recipe for the filling will make extra, and you can freeze it and make another one later on.

In this series, we have looked at all aspects of raising a self-reliant flock of chickens — everything from housing to feeding to incubating eggs. I hope these are helpful to you, as we make all make our quest towards independence.

Feeding the flock

By Charles Sanders

As we discuss feeding your chickens, know that they can get a lot of supplemental nutrition from foraging about the yard and homestead. Insects, worms, grit, and grains are all picked up and contribute to the fat fryers and golden-yolked eggs that put store-bought eggs to shame. If at all possible, I believe that your chickens should be allowed to forage about for their food for at least part of the day. That said, your chicken flock will still need to be fed. In this article, I will discuss some whats, whens, and whys in feeding your poultry flock.

Getting started

First off, the moment your new chicks arrive, it's important to have a good chick starter mash available to them. They are going to be hungry and you should have their feed in place as you put them in the brooder. You can help to ensure the baby chicks will peck and begin to feed by placing a few ordinary glass marbles in the feeder along with the feed. The birds will peck at the bright colors and soon get the idea.

Feed this starter to your birds until they are about 8 weeks old. At that time, switch them to a good growing ration. This feed has just a slightly lower percentage of protein, but still contributes to good growth in your birds. Keep them on this feed until they are about 18-20 weeks of age.

Laying feed

Once your laying hens reach 18-20 weeks of age, it's time to get them to shift gears into egg-laying mode. You can encourage and benefit this time in their lives by feeding them a good laying ration. This feed supplies their nutritional needs during the egg-laying cycle, as

These new chicks peck at a pan of chick starter.

There are no eggs as good as those produced right on your own place, by your own birds.

well as provide extra calcium that is needed for eggshell development.

This is probably a good time to mention that regardless of which feed your birds are being fed, be sure to also provide them with a source of grit. That rough material is needed in their gizzards for proper digestion of their food. If your birds are allowed to be on the ground during all or part of the day, they will probably be getting plenty of grit as they forage. Otherwise, a pan or box of sandy, gravelly grit should be made available.

In addition, once your birds begin laying, be sure to provide a source for crushed oyster shell for them to consume. The crushed shell will help provide even more calcium for them as they produce eggs. Crushed oyster shell is available where you get your feed and can be placed in a container right alongside the feed trough.

There are several good brands of feeds and rations for the home poultry raiser to consider for their flock.

Nutrena

Nutrena is a long-time producer of livestock feeds. They offer a variety of feeds for the flock, including some feeds that are "natural and vegetarian." Below is a list of their offerings:

- NatureWise® — Natural, vegetarian feeds for your flock
- Chick Starter Grower Crumbles
- Chick Starter Grower Medicated Crumbles
- Layer 16% Feed
- Feather Fixer
- Meatbird Crumbles
- All Flock Pellets
- Scratch Grains
- Country Feeds®
- Chick Starter Grower Crumbles
- Chick Starter Grower Medicated Crumbles
- Layer 16% Feed
- All Flock Pellets
- Meatbird Crumbles
- Scratch Grains

Purina Mills

Purina Mills is another old standby brand that offers a wide selection of feeds for the home poultry raiser. Here is a list of the products they offer:

- Start & Grow
- Flock Raiser
- Layena
- Layena Plus Omega-3
- Scratch Grains
- Flock Block — A whole grain supplement for free-range poultry that also contains oyster shell and grit.
- Show Chow Broiler Complete

The products of either of these producers are probably available in your area. There are many more good regional producers of poultry feeds that you may know of or learn about as you begin your poultry-raising adventure. The important thing is that the feeds have good formulation, consistent production, and high quality ingredients.

Homemade formula

Some folks want to have more control over the ingredients that go into the feeds that their flock consumes. I don't recommend feeding homemade formulas for a few reasons. First, consistency is important. Switching ingredients or even sources for the same ingredients can have an adverse effect on your birds. Second, it is often difficult to grow or locate all the ingredients that are required for a good, balanced poultry feed. Third, it is generally more economical to purchase balanced poultry feeds, then supplement them with home-raised produce, scraps, forages, and so forth. Your flock will still be getting the needed nutrition and you will be supplying a respectable portion of their diet as well.

If you do decide to try your hand at creating your own feeds for your birds, here is a good basic formula:

Chickens feeding on scraps from the garden and kitchen

Chicken feed for layers

50 lb. cracked wheat
50 lb. cracked corn
50 lb. oats
50 lb. fish meal
10 lb. ground oyster shells
2 lb. salt

When it comes to feeding scraps, you can feed just about any leftover plant material from the garden to the birds. After canning or preparing vegetables for eating, the scraps will be welcomed by the flock. Overripe or damaged vegetables can be tossed in and will soon be devoured. Just keep an eye on the birds and don't overwhelm them with produce. Let them clean it up before throwing more in.

In the photo on the left, you can see our flock of young chickens made up of Rhode Island Reds, Buff Orpingtons, and Silver-Laced Wyandottes. They are feeding on grass clippings, cabbage leaves, watermelon rinds, and assorted scraps from the kitchen and garden. The scraps are very nutritious and the birds love them.

Storing feed

Finally, have a good place to store your chicken feed where mice and other vermin can't get into it. I use an ordinary galvanized garbage can. The lid fits tightly on the can and is a good, manageable size. If you have a lot of feed to store, consider converting an old chest freezer into a feed bin. Just set the bags of feed in the freezer cabinet and close the lid. We used one of these for years to keep the feed dry and rodent-free.

As you feed your birds, spend time with them and enjoy the experience of having your own home flock. It will be worth the effort.

Train your chickens
(and other livestock)

By Kenny Coogan

For those of us who have livestock in the backyard, our feathered and furry friends are often the highlight for visitors. All the attention turns to the animals, as they preen, cluck, coo, and carry on. It is amusing when our sheep act like humans and when our poultry act like sheep. What my friends find most remarkable is when my livestock perform on cue. I have trained many farm animals including chickens, babydoll Southdown sheep, a Devon milking cow, and two 500-pound Berkshire pigs. It may seem frivolous to some, but there is a great motive: it allows me to easily care for them when needed.

Targeting might be the most beneficial behavior you train your livestock to do. When an animal "targets," you are asking them to aim a body part towards a specific object. Once trained, this behavior has endless possibilities.

A skittish animal, like a horse or chicken, could be trained to approach visitors by moving towards a target that the guests are holding. The target is familiar and positive to the animal and reduces the anxiety associated with new people. An added benefit is that when the animal targets they are not directly approaching the new person, which is usually the most intimidating part. This makes it easy for you to pass off the target to many different people and still get the same response from your farm animal. Introducing your now-friendly herd to more potential customers on your farm tour just got easier!

Targets usually look like a ball attached to a stick. For farm animals (chickens, turkeys, cows, and mules), I have used a tennis ball at

A cochin hen leaving from a stump station to author's hand voluntarily.

the end of a ½-inch wide, one-foot long PVC pipe. I cut an X into the tennis ball and it fit so tightly on the pipe I didn't need to use adhesive. For smaller animals, a target could be as simple as a piece of paper or a small square of AstroTurf.

To start training, present your target to the animal. Curious animals will come over and investigate. Once they place their muzzle on the target, reward them with a small treat. For large livestock I have used a small handful of their sweet grain. For pigs I have used fresh vegetables, spoonfuls of yogurt, or small amounts of popcorn or cereal. After the animal enjoys their treat, wait until their nose bumps into the target again and then reward with another small amount of food. After a few repetitions, try to move the target a few inches. Then try a few feet. The animal will quickly start following the ball, so they can get the much anticipated reward.

Using target training, I have trained my Berkshire pigs to run through a hula-hoop, my babydoll Southdown sheep to give kisses, spin to the right, turn to the left, and jump over hurdles. The mule and cow shift from one stall to another and all of them are also trained to stand still in one place. This allows for voluntary physical and visual exams on them as needed. Casting the cow and physical restraint is no longer needed.

The cow and mule will voluntarily lift their legs to touch the target and come running in from pasture when they see it — the farrier sure appreciates the training. The visitors to my small farm think it is really impressive, but the training serves a vital purpose. What behaviors are you going to accomplish with target training?

Creating multiple targets that look different is something I did a few years ago with much success. I trained one female leghorn that had a black leg band to target to a black piece of laminated paper. I then trained another leghorn with a white leg band to station to a white piece of paper. During the training session, I left the non-rewarding station in the area. If they accidently went to it, nothing happened.

Target training a Berkshire pig

Here is a Narragansett turkey stationing on a yellow piece of paper.

No punishment, but also no rewards. After a week or so I could have two visitors each take a station and run around the yard with their perfectly matched chicken following them. If you want to try this with multiple chickens, using different colors, textures, or patterns are some other possibilities.

If you create identical targets, you can train your livestock for long agility paths. Creating agility equipment like weave poles, hurdles, or platforms does not have to be expensive. Use whatever leftover materials you have, such as

PVC tubes or old picture frames, to create a frugal yet practical agility course, something very fitting for a small farm. Placing a few stations along the path should give your animals an idea on how to go from point A to B to C. At each target be sure to give them a little encouragement (treats). If you find your animals skipping targets, move the targets a little closer to set them up for success. By giving them a few treats once they have hit their targets and through repetition, your birds will learn the course. As they become more familiar with the path you can start making the targets farther apart, eventually reinforcing longer distances.

Using the techniques outlined here, it won't be long before your livestock are fully engaged in this no-coercion training. Training your animals to target is not only a great way to bond with them, it also makes taking care of them easier and allows for mental and physical stimulation.

Raising squab for meat

By Allen Easterly

There a lot of people that have never heard the term "squab" before. Even of those that have, many know very little about them. The truth is, squab is just another name for pigeon. Those raised for the table are usually a special breed, not the pigeons in the park pooping on our statues and eating scrap food people give them. While the adult birds can be eaten and are still referred to as squab, it's the young birds that usually provide the best table fare.

On my farm in the heart of the Shenandoah Valley of Virginia, I have spent the last six years developing a hobby farm raising meat chickens, rabbits, and quail. Selling at farmers' markets gives my farm and products exposure to folks from all walks of life from near and far. Last year, a local chef bought some of my quail and prepared a special dinner for other chefs in the Washington, D.C. area. Chef talk being what it is, they got to discussing squab and how hard it is come by. The chefs were going all the way to New York or North Carolina to get their birds. The quality was always somewhat questionable and not always consistent as any good chef would require. So they asked if I would be willing to raise squab for them, providing a local source. I went full steam ahead researching, planning, and building a flock of squab to meet their demands and also to give me a few to sell at farmers' markets. I've had some successes and some failures, but I'm learning more every day.

Selecting your breed

While there are many breeds of pigeon available, most are for show or racing. There are very few good meat pigeon breeds available. The Red Carneau and Red Giant Runt are sometimes available from breeders, but the White King Utility is the most popular and most easily obtained. I chose to raise White Kings for two simple reasons: they are white, and they are large, fast-growing birds. Dark-feathered birds can leave "tattoo" marks in the skin when the feathers are removed. For presentation purposes, chefs want a clean looking bird. White Kings are larger pigeons; they grow to weigh nearly a pound during the first month of life, and two pounds upon reaching adulthood.

Be prepared to fork out some cash because these birds are expensive and can run from $50-$60 each from a big hatchery. However, I have seen them advertised by private breeders for as low as $20 each. Shipping costs are also

A 60-watt light bulb in the hole of the concrete block provides enough heat to keep the water in the rubber container thawed.

Sources for squab breeder birds

- www.strombergschickens.com
- www.tonkbranchfarm.com
- www.kingpigeons.com

Feed sources:

Brown's Premium Pigeon Feed
www.fmbrown.com/catalogs_2013/PigeonCatalog090513.pdf

Jones Seed Company
www.jones-seed.com/c-6-pigeon.aspx

Nutriblend
www.lumber2.com/NutriBlend-Gold-Pigeon-Feed-p/pm0001388.htm

significant since there are special needs for live adult birds. If you can find birds within reasonable driving distance, it would probably pay to just pick them up yourself. Most of the cheaper birds from private breeders don't come with any guarantee, while the hatchery birds usually come with a guarantee that they are purebred, delivered alive, accurate sexing, and some will guarantee mated pairs. Accurate sexing is important because it's impossible to determine sex just by looking at their hoo-hoo. Sex is most often determined by considerable observation of courting and mating behavior. It's important to also obtain mated pairs because pigeons mate for life.

Housing and nests

It is worth your investment to build a strong, sound coop to house your birds. Design your coop to allow at least four square feet of floor space per breeding pair. The more room you give them, the better. Give the coop a southern exposure for optimum daylight and warmth during winter. A wired-in outdoor flyway is also important for the birds to obtain fresh air and some exercise. The best floor for the indoor portion of the coop is concrete. It can be cleaned fairly easily and hosed out from time to time. Due to cost, I decided to use plywood for my coop and it seems to be doing fine as long as it is kept dry and bird waste shoveled out when needed as with any floor. The birds do much better in a clean environment. Keeping the coop clean helps prevent the birds from contracting respiratory illnesses and other diseases. For a roof over the coop end, I used plastic roofing panels in white and blue. The blue is transparent and the white opaque. Both allow plenty of light to enter the coop. When constructing your coop, make sure it is strong and well-built to protect your bird investment. The flyway frame should be covered with heavy-gauge welded wire to prevent predators from entering. Occasionally I'll hear a loud bang in the vicinity of my coop. Upon investigation, I usually see a hawk recovering from a high-speed crash into the wire from its attempt to take a pigeon out for lunch. I used ½-inch heavy hardware cloth which also works well to keep out mice and snakes. Both will eat the eggs from a nest and snakes will also consume young birds, not to mention scare the bejeebers out of you when you check a nest box! Make sure there are no openings or gaps where wire meets wood or these critters will wiggle their way through.

Nest box size requirements are 16x12x16-inches with an additional 8-inch wide platform just outside the box for the birds to land. Most of my research indicates that two nest boxes are required for each pair of birds, the reason being that the female will leave a nest of young to lay eggs in an adjoining nest box and start incubation again. The male takes care of the first batch of young until they can leave the nest. But my experience indicates that this is not always the case. I haven't seen any of my birds reproduce that quickly. That doesn't mean that they won't someday, they just haven't done so yet. Add some nesting material to each box or scatter it on the floor of the coop for the birds to use in building their own nests. Pine needles or straw work very well, if they are clean and dry. Pigeons don't build much of a nest like most songbirds do. The nest is generally just a shallow depression in an unorganized pile of nesting material. It seems to work just fine for the fast-growing chicks.

Food and water

Of all the critters I raise on my farm, the pigeons require the highest investment in feed. For successful breeding, they need a high protein (minimum 13.5%) premium pigeon feed for best results. The parent birds feed their young pigeon "milk" — regurgitated, partially-digested food — that needs to be high in protein for proper growth and strength of the young birds. I've found that any feed you can find with a large amount of peas and safflower is the most sought after by the pigeons. They will eat corn, millet, and other grains, but only after the good stuff is gone. And they're not too anxious to eat the less desirable seeds. During the off-breeding season it might be necessary to hold back giving fresh feed until they clean their plate. Maple peas, Austrian peas, and Canadian peas are the most common found in quality pigeon feed. Check with your local feed store and see what they have or what they can order. I have to special order my feed because no one else around here raises squab. I've tried giving them a high protein chicken feed that is supposed to be appropriate for pigeons as well, but my birds just won't eat it. Keep an ample supply of feed available for the birds at all times. Any stress from hunger can negatively effect egg laying and baby growth.

As with any animal you raise, fresh clean water daily is very important to maintaining healthy birds. Pigeons should also be given clean bathing water on a daily basis. Not only should the water be clean and fresh, but the container should also be given a good wipe-down. Without this extra step, bacteria will begin to multiply rapidly, leaving a slimy coating in the water vessels. Keeping fresh water available can be a challenge in winter. To solve this problem I purchased a black rubber feed pan from the local feed store and set it up on a concrete block with the holes facing up. In one of the holes of the block I put a 60-watt light bulb and plugged it into a timer. I set the timer to come on a couple hours before daylight and then at hourly intervals every other hour until sunset. The heat from the bulb warms the pan, keeping the water thawed enough for the birds to drink. The black pan also absorbs heat from the sun to help keep the water thawed. In addition, I also placed a fairly large protruding rock in the center for the birds to land on. The rock also absorbs heat from the bulb and retains it longer, keeping the water thawed. Unfortunately, 60-watt bulbs are not easy to find in this country any longer, but you can run a couple lower watt bulbs to obtain the same results.

Breeding

Pigeons are warm weather breeders and will only reproduce during the warmer months of the year. You'll know when to expect eggs when you see the males puff up their necks and strut their stuff to encourage their lifetime mate to hit the straw and lay a couple eggs. The female will lay one egg, and a day or so later, will lay another. She will then begin incubating the eggs for 17 days until they hatch. Her hubby will help with the incubation as well so she can get a bite to eat and some exercise. Once the chicks hatch, both parents participate

Author's coop is 12x12 feet with a 144-square-foot flyway. The coop can hold 36 pairs of birds.

in feeding and keeping the young warm and protected. The young chicks and nest should not be disturbed except to remove the occasional dead chick. Two weeks after her first clutch hatches, the female is supposed to start another nest in an adjoining nest box and lay a couple more eggs. This is what my research tells me; however, my personal experience is that they start another nest whenever they get around to it, and that is usually after a little vacation. Your experience may be different.

Preparing squab for the table

Squab are ready to be removed from the nest and processed at just 28 days of age. The good thing about that is you haven't had to feed them a single grain. Mom and Pop have been taking care of that for you. The birds should be removed from the parents the day before processing to give their crop time to empty; otherwise you will have a mess on your hands at processing time. The best way to bring them to their demise is to cut the jugular vein just under the jaw. The use of a killing cone will be useful and will prevent the meat from bruising. They will pass quickly. Since the birds are so young, they have very little body feathers. The under-wing should be fully feathered by this age, but most of what covers them is down which does not come off very well in a plucking machine. Your best bet is to dry pick the birds. Scalding should not be necessary, but if you believe it would help, dunk them in 150 degree water for about 50 seconds. The main thing about scalding is not to use too high a temperature or dunk too long, or else you will end up partially cooking the bird. This will also make the skin much more tender and prone to tear easily when plucking. The next step is to remove the head and feet, then remove the neck. Make a small slit in the abdomen and remove the innards. Make sure you get the crop and windpipe. Save the neck, heart, and cleaned gizzard if you wish. Rinse the bird in clean cold water. The results should give you a finished bird between 13 and 16 ounces. If you are not going to eat the bird within a few days, it should be vacuum-sealed and frozen. Fresh birds benefit from a couple days in the refrigerator, allowing rigor mortis to subside and the muscle fibers to relax, resulting in a more tender bird.

Squab is a plump, moist, tender dark meat bird. Some folks say it tastes like dark meat chicken. Others say it's a cross between chicken and duck. The meat is lean and the skin is fatty; it is very high in protein, minerals, and vitamins (see nutrition facts below). The young birds are great for grilling or roasting using your favorite chicken or duck recipe. Suggested grilling time is 20-35 minutes, and roasting time is 25-35 minutes. Older birds, being larger, have much firmer flesh and are best used in casseroles or crock pot dishes.

No matter how you cook your squab, you are sure to enjoy eating them as well as raising them. The adult White Kings are large, beautiful, pure white birds that are very interesting to watch and fun to care for. Give them good housing with a flyway for exercise, the best food you can find, plenty of fresh water, and an occasional coop cleaning and you'll have a great time raising these gentle birds. They'll repay you with fine delicacy dining usually reserved as a high-end menu item in restaurants.

Keep your chickens healthy

(And what to do if they're not)

By Jackie Clay-Atkinson

Fortunately, chickens are among the easiest homestead livestock to raise. Given basic care, they'll happily sing, scratch the soil, and lay plenty of eggs for your family. Most people, though, do harbor the nagging worry, "What will I do if my chicken gets sick? And how will I even know if it is?"

Really, it's quite simple. A healthy chicken is active. It eats, drinks, and dashes around looking for tasty morsels. Its eyes are bright, its nostrils are clear with no dirt or mucus, its comb is a bright red (except during molt when it sometimes gets pale), there is no poop clinging to its rear end, and its legs are smooth and clean. The feathers of a healthy chicken are tight and smooth (although some breeds like Frizzles have fuzzy feathers normally). All chickens molt at least twice a year and during that time, their feathers go from patchy to bald in spots. This is normal. But if all of your chickens suddenly start pecking at their feathers, this is *not* normal. If one chicken starts sitting around puffed up, this is also a sign of a problem.

Before you read further, know that although chickens can get many different diseases, they actually very seldom do. I've had chickens for more than half a century and have only had three or four that became ill. And these were, in most cases, quickly and efficiently treated.

Predators

Predators actually cause the most chicken deaths. The most common predators are foxes, coyotes, raccoons, mink, owls, hawks, wea-

It's best to prevent predator injuries or deaths by fencing your birds in a large, tight wire pen. If raptors are around, such as owls and hawks, adding a net top is also a good idea.

sels, and feral cats. Consider keeping your free-range birds in a large, fenced area and locking them in a tight coop with a wooden or cement floor come nighttime. The birds that aren't killed outright often suffer terrible wounds from predators. One of our hen turkeys tried to protect her babies from a fox who got inside our barn through a three-inch crack (he was extremely emaciated). He killed all of the babies and tore a big hole in the mother turkey. We got the fox the next night and treated the turkey with antibiotics. She healed up and went on to have another brood this year.

Weather

Heat and cold can both kill chickens, but dying of heat is more common. When the temperature gets above 100° F, your chickens should have access to cooling shade and a good breeze. Adding a fan to the coop is sometimes essential during hot spells. You can lose many birds on one hot day if they are left in a coop with poor ventilation. During periods of heat, it is absolutely essential that they have access to cool, fresh water at all times. Simple preventative steps such as adding a tarp or shade cloth over a corner of the run will prevent heat stroke and death.

As we live in the cold north, we have been asked many times what we do to keep our chickens and turkeys from freezing. The answer is providing lots of wood shavings for bedding, having enough birds in a relatively small coop with a low roof so their body heat keeps it warmer, and making sure that all cracks are covered before cold weather hits. We are going to build an insulated coop soon so that our birds enjoy winter more but with even our minimal care, we have healthy, happy poultry all winter long.

Just because water freezes in the winter, don't let them depend on snow for "water." Take them out a pail of warm water twice a day, dumping out any ice before adding to their container. Having a shallow rubber pan works great as you can easily break out the ice without damaging the pan.

In cold climates, large-combed breeds often freeze their combs during the winter when living in coops that are too cold. Although the comb dies and turns black, eventually falling off, the bird will not suffer any long-term distress. So if you live where the winters get cold, you might consider raising pea-combed breeds.

If you have electricity available, you can also add a heat lamp above the perches (where the birds can't reach it to peck) and a heated base for your water container so they always have lukewarm water to drink. These are greatly appreciated by your flock. If you use a heat lamp, wire or chain it to a sturdy screw eye in a rafter so it can't get knocked down. Coop fires from heat lamps are all too common.

Parasites

I'd say that parasites are one of the most common homestead poultry problems. No, it's not usually worms, but mites or lice. Signs of these biting insects are rough feathers and birds that peck and pull at their feathers a lot. If you catch a chicken and look closely, you can see either larger lice or tiny moving mites. If left untreated, the birds will become stressed and will sometimes suffer from anemia and die.

Luckily, treatment is pretty easy. All birds should have access to a dust bath. This can be chicken-made (they love to dig depressions in the dirt or your flower bed and will fluff and flutter happily in that) or person-made. You can fill a larger shallow container with sand and even add diatomaceous earth if you wish. The "dust" helps keep the birds free from mites and lice.

If this is not enough, you can take stronger measures. Clean all bedding out of the coop, chase the birds outside, and spray the inside of the coop with pyrethrins, including inside the nest boxes. Close the coop up tight and then catch the birds, one by one, and hold them upside down and dust with pyrethrin powder. This is non-toxic and will kill the parasites. Once all have been dosed, let them return to the re-bedded coop and resume normal life. Usually one dose will do the trick but keep an eye on them for the next two weeks, just to be sure. If you see more signs of parasites or the mites/lice again, repeat.

Another common problem in flocks is scaly leg. Instead of nice, smooth legs, a chicken develops scales up and down the leg, right down to the toes. The cause is tiny mites that burrow into the cracks between the natural scales of a bird's legs, causing large scales to form. Luckily this ugly condition can easily be treated. Just take a clean soup can full of warmed up mineral or cod-liver oil to your coop and gently pick up each affected bird and dip the whole leg into the oil. You can use an old, clean paintbrush to reach any part that is not soaked. Let the leg drip well and repeat with the other leg. Turn the bird loose and repeat with any other infested birds. Usually one or two treatments is all that is necessary. The oil not only smothers the mites but helps smooth the legs.

A common protozoa causes common coccidiosis in poultry. This is a fairly common disease in younger chicks, especially. The signs are diarrhea, lethargy, and lack of appetite. They usually become infected by crowding in unsanitary surroundings or drinking water fouled by fecal material. Keep your chickens clean, warm, and dry, and they probably will never have this problem.

Should your birds show symptoms, collect a very fresh sample of the droppings and take it immediately to your veterinarian for examination under a microscope. They can tell you exactly what medication will quickly take care of it. Usually a coccidiostat is available at local feed and farm stores as well, if you have no veterinarian available. These are usually in powder or liquid form and are added to the poultry's water or mixed and given by eye dropper to your sick birds.

Respiratory diseases

Upper respiratory diseases are fairly common in chickens, especially those without regular access to clean outdoor runs. Dust, wood shavings, and dry litter can all initiate irritation that can lead to bronchitis, pneumonia,

Healthy chickens are active and have smooth feathers and legs, clean rear ends, and bright, shining combs.

or laryngotracheitis. Once the bird's respiratory tract becomes irritated, it is easy to pick up infections. Avoid drafts, cold conditions, and dampness in the coop, and you'll head off respiratory diseases. I haven't had a bird with a respiratory disease in more than 30 years.

Should one of your birds seem to have trouble breathing or have mucus discharge from its nostrils, immediately bring it to a warm, isolated spot (a cage in the house works well) and begin treatment with a powdered antibiotic such as tetracycline or sulfa. If spotted quickly, these symptoms usually can be resolved within a few days.

Egg-bound hens

Being egg bound can happen to a hen now and then. Usually it's a pullet that begins to lay an egg that is too large for her to pass. But sometimes it can occur with a mature hen. If you can see the egg, simply puncture the egg with a nail and then with a lubricated finger, gently crush the shell so that you don't injure her. If not, you should be able to touch the egg by reaching a lubricated finger (use petroleum jelly or dish soap) up her vent. Insert a baby ear syringe into the vent and deposit warm mineral oil around the egg. Then by pushing gently on her abdomen, you can usually help the egg out. An egg-bound hen will sit in the nest box for prolonged periods with no egg, refusing to come out for feed or water. If you cannot feel an egg with your finger, that probably isn't her problem.

Pecking

Pecking can be a problem both with baby chicks and adults. Any sign of blood can initiate pecking. Some other frequent causes are crowding, boredom, and being overly warm. This pecking can become quite brutal, ending in the death and cannibalization of birds. It is easier to prevent than cure. Be sure your birds have adequate room in the pen or coop with a large run they can access year-round. Even here in the north, we let our birds out into our orchard on all but very cold, blustery days. Give them plenty of bedding to scratch around in and keep the feeder full. If you have a bird that suddenly shows feathers picked off, and blood showing, immediately remove it until it is healed. Then bring it back during the night when there is less light in the coop so it can "stay in the shadows" away from other birds until they get used to it. If chicks start to pick at each other, check to see if the temperature in the pen is too high. Then add more room to the pen and give them some scratch feed to dig and peck at in addition to their chick mash. Sometimes using a red heat lamp will also help keep chicks from picking.

As I've said, poultry are usually very healthy and if you don't often bring in new birds or travel to poultry shows and poultry swaps, your chance of having healthy poultry is very good. If you end up with a sick bird, call an experienced local poultry raiser or your veterinarian right away for help. Most poultry health issues can easily be dealt with by home care. If you would like more information, I highly recommend buying *Storey's Guide to Raising Chickens* by Gail Damerow and *A Veterinary Guide For All Animal Owners* by C.E. Spauding D.V.M and Jackie Clay.

Feeding and watering your chickens

By Jackie Clay-Atkinson

Although chickens are probably the easiest of all homestead livestock to raise, there is a lot of debate on the right way to feed and water them. Of course, commercial feed companies would like you to think that if you don't use their bagged feed, your birds will either die outright or simply not do well. But when you think back to what our grandparents and *their* grandparents fed their flocks, you'll quickly see this is a fallacy. While it is easier to simply go to the feed store and buy a bag of feed, that's not your only option.

Baby chicks

I'll admit that when we buy a new batch of baby chicks to brood at home, we usually pick up a bag of commercial crumbled, processed chick starter simply for the ease of getting the babies off to a good start. But what about our mama hens that have hidden a nest of eggs in a remote location and come off their nest with a dozen fluffy chicks? We don't feed them chick starter; they just range with the hen and eat the tasty morsels she scratches up. And she does this all day, every day. And our hen-raised baby chicks do as well (if not better) than the pampered, commercially-fed brooder chicks.

When you have decided to feed your baby chicks a commercial crumble in their brooder, have it ready when you bring them home. Sprinkle some on their bedding, as a chick's first instinct is to pick up food from the ground. They will quickly learn to eat from a trough-style chick feeder. For every 50 birds, you need about two feet of feeder. Choose a feeder that has a rod or plastic that turns freely over the tray of feed so the chicks can't roost over the feed or get into the trough and scratch it out into the bedding.

In addition to the feed, be sure you provide your chicks with grit in another feed trough-type container, so they will be able to digest their feed well. With the commercial feed, this may not be as critical, but it is important, espe-

Our chickens choose much of their own food in our acre-plus orchard. Here, they're scratching some of the rotted manure mulch around our young trees.

All summer and into the fall, I take baskets into the garden to gather less-than-perfect tomatoes and other crops that the chickens love. Below, my friend Sue enjoys feeding extra tomatoes to her free-range Black Australorps.

cially if you sprinkle some cracked grain in with their processed feed.

For water, we use a screw-on waterer that fastens onto a quart canning jar. You will probably want one for each 25 chicks. These keep the water clean and prevent chicks from getting into the water and possibly drowning. As they grow, they'll drink more water, so we switch to a plastic one-gallon waterer that has a screw-on tray.

Keep feed in front of your chicks at all times. However, when you raise Cornish Rock meat birds, it is usually recommended that you remove their feed in the evening after about 12 days to avoid leg problems. It is also a good idea to provide them with a nutritional supplement in either the feed or water such as Broiler Booster that has additional vitamins, minerals, and electrolytes aimed at keeping fast-growing birds healthy.

Raising pullets or meat birds

As soon as the chicks have feathered out, you will be able to switch them over to either a commercial grower ration, which is crumbled and processed like the chick starter is, or a feed-mill mixture often called 18% poultry feed. This has high enough protein to let the chicks continue with good growth and feathering out but won't fatten the meat birds so much that they develop heart conditions (which can cause instant death). If you are raising pullets to be layers, it's wise to boost that up to a 20% protein ration.

We have always used local mixes, as we don't like using commercial feeds containing antibiotics and other drugs that are not necessary in home-raised small flocks. I have nothing against treating birds with antibiotics if they are sick and need antibiotics, but I don't like giving drugs routinely.

Be sure your growing birds have access to both grit (ours get plenty digging in the sand and gravel in our orchard) and oyster shell for good future egg production and bone development.

We provide water to our mixed flock during the spring, summer, and fall months via a self-watering bowl that is plumbed into a 300-gallon water tank. As the chickens drink, the bowl refills with clean, fresh water. If the bowl should get dirty, it's easily disengaged and rinsed out. This way, we only have to fill the tank perhaps twice a summer. If you don't have a big tank, you can also use a plastic food-grade 55-gallon barrel as a holding tank. There are several other "self-waterers" available from such companies as Nasco Farm & Ranch and Murray McMurray Hatchery. Some attach to a garden hose, while others can be fed from a large container such as a plastic barrel or large water cooler.

In the winter, you can provide water for your flock in various ways. One of the best is to install a heated waterer. This lets you keep up to three gallons of fresh water warm even during the coldest weather. Unfortunately, we live off-grid and do not have that option. So we keep a large, shallow rubber feed pan in the coop and carry a bucket of warm water out to the birds twice a day. The rubber pan is easily whacked and flexed so any clinging ice is easily broken out before we refill the pan.

Alternative feeds

Despite what the chicken food companies want you to think, chicken feed can be found right on the homestead. Remember, each and every bite of feed the chickens get that has been raised at home is a bite you didn't have to buy.

While we do keep a feeder full of 18% poultry grain in the coop, we reduce our feed bill a whole lot by feeding foods grown right here on our homestead. When our birds range in the orchard, they pick up lots of insects, especially grasshoppers and flies (protein), fallen fruit (vitamins), and plenty of clover and grass. As harvest season comes nearer, they love to munch on tomatoes that have a bad spot or have been stepped on, extra summer squash, spinach, kale, and comfrey leaves.

As the season progresses, they get lots of tomato skins/seeds, carrot leaves, pepper "guts," and immature winter squash that are too small to keep for storage.

After harvest, we feed our chickens the seeds from our pumpkins and squash. They get any part of the squash that we don't use, including any immature seeds. You'd laugh to see those chickens rushing to the door when they see a pumpkin or squash! We also give them any of our "extra" ears of sweet corn to pick through that we haven't let mature for drying.

Of course, all year long, our chickens get most of our kitchen waste (stale bread, crushed egg shells, peelings, leftover vegetables, sour milk, etc.), housed in an ice cream bucket on the counter and emptied daily.

We also give our poultry a healthy helping of either extra milk (usually skimmed) or whey from cheese making, poured right in their rubber winter watering container. Boy, do they scarf that down in a hurry! Around our homestead, you can never have too much milk.

In the winter, I often gather up the fine leaves left over from when I open a bale of alfalfa or trefoil hay, bring them inside, and soak them overnight in boiling water to soften and cook them. The chickens love them, come morning, and this treat also encourages them to lay more in the winter.

If you're worried about a balanced diet, you can easily add a protein supplement such as soybean meal or even chopped garden peas, which are high in protein, to their diet. There is a wide variety of vitamins available in many home-raised foods. Left on their own with a good area to range in, it's surprising how well chickens will balance their own diet.

Foods that chickens should not be fed

Although chickens will eat about anything, there are a few foods they should never have. Never feed them anything that is toxic. Please don't feed your chickens (or any other critters) rhubarb leaves. They are very poisonous! So are those beautiful castor beans you grow in your flower bed.

Don't give your birds fat or meat scraps from the table. They can cause digestive upsets. Fresh meat can also encourage cannibalism.

There is a debate as to whether to offer chickens potato peelings. We do and have never seen any ill effects, but others say that chickens don't digest them if the peels are uncooked.

Feeding chickens raw, cracked whole eggs often stimulates them to begin eating their own eggs, as well as their flock-mates'. If you want to feed your chickens eggs, boil, poach, or otherwise cook them before feeding.

Feeding poultry doesn't have to be rocket science. People just like you have been doing it for generations.

Keeping chickens in town

By Dotty DeVille

When my husband and I retired, our finances and our physical abilities limited our choices of where to live. We ended up living in a small town to be near our son and our grandchildren. Our house is decently-sized, but our backyard is probably only a quarter acre, and we are surrounded by houses on all sides.

Knowing all this, some might be surprised that we are proud owners of a backyard flock of chickens. In our town ordinances, it doesn't say anything specifically about chickens, but it does say that if anyone complains about loud noises, that thing making the noise will not be allowed. So let me tell you how we do it.

Keep the noise down

The biggest complaint most people have about chickens is that they are noisy. When my husband built our coop, he made sure to use thick wood to muffle any chicken sounds. While we do have a window for ventilation, he put a sliding plexiglass sheet in there, which lets us close it at night and easily slide it open in the morning.

We do have a rooster, because the benefits of fertilized eggs are too great to pass up. To keep the rooster under the neighbors' radar, we fitted him with a No-Crow Collar. These collars are only about $12, and they lessen the noise and reduce the frequency of the rooster's crowing. With the collar on, a hen cackling over her egg is a louder sound than the rooster's crow!

Keeping the rooster quiet is key to having chickens in town.

Who could resist this cute source of fresh eggs?

Bribe the neighbors

There is nothing better to keep neighbors happy than a basket of fresh eggs. When we first moved in, we only had one neighbor in the house next to us. She enjoyed the happy chicken sounds, and let us know that they would never bother her. But, when folks started moving in to the houses around us, we had no idea if they would be okay with our chickens or not. So, as a "welcome to the neighborhood" present, we would show up at their door with a dozen fresh eggs. Thus far, no one has complained, because they know without our chickens, they wouldn't get free, delicious, farm-fresh eggs.

No free-ranging

Nothing turns a neighbor into an enemy faster than a wayward chicken digging up their prize-winning tulips! Not to mention all the little "presents" a chicken leaves on doorsteps, sidewalks, and lawns. Instead of allowing your chickens to run free, make them a nice fenced-in run. I did this for my flock, and it keeps the chickens in the backyard, while still allowing them to scratch around in the dirt.

Clean regularly

The other problem neighbors might have is the smell of a coop long overdue for a cleaning. If cleaned out properly and regularly, a coop will have no smell. I like to clean mine out once a week in the summer, but I do the deep bedding method in the winter. Instead of cleaning the coop out, you just sprinkle more straw (or whatever bedding you use) over the old bedding each week. The dirty bedding on the bottom composts itself, which gets rid of the smell and adds extra heat during the cold months.

Conclusion

It's really very easy to have chickens in town, provided you are in accordance with the laws. And if there are ordinances expressly forbidding chickens, these can always be changed. There are quite a few people that have managed to petition the laws in their towns. Good luck!

Free-range chickens

Problems and solutions

By Donna Insco

Many farmsteads can benefit from a flock of free-range laying hens. But some things must be considered before letting your flock out of the coop. A free-ranging flock is not recommended if you have close neighbors. Your birds will not recognize property lines and you can't expect a neighbor to fence his property to keep your birds out. Some breeds of poultry wander farther than others. I remember my grandmother's guineas would go out in the field 150 yards from the house. However, my New Hampshires and Rhode Island Reds never get more than 50 yards away. Another thing to consider is the proximity of neighboring dogs, since they will likely be the predators that cause the most concern. In many areas, free-running dogs outnumber the local population of wild predators.

Advantages

For me, the benefits of free-range birds outweigh the disadvantages. The price of 50 pounds of laying mash has nearly tripled since I started keeping chickens, and the price continues to climb. Allowing birds to forage for some of their own food reduces the costs of keeping them. In summer, my hens can get approximately half of their food by patrolling the yard, pasture, edge of the woods, and barnyard.

Free-range birds suppress ticks, ants, and crop pests such as caterpillars and grasshoppers. Chickens relish these pests as tasty morsels. Their constant scratching in the dirt helps prevent some insect eggs from hatching by uncovering them and causing the eggs to dry out in the sun and wind.

Free-ranging poultry can also function as alarm systems. Guineas will raise a fuss if any-

Rhode Island Red pullets enjoying some sunshine in the driveway

thing unusual catches their attention. Guineas and chickens also dislike snakes, and will sometimes let you know when one is near. My hens have a peculiar cackle when a snake is close by. Once, the flock had a snake surrounded and backed up against the truck tire. From a distance, it looked like a copperhead, but turned out to be a harmless hognose.

Disadvantages (and solutions)

Roaming chickens can cause problems, however. They will completely destroy young plants in a garden. They will jump upwards to remove tomatoes and berries from established vines, as well as peck holes in turnips, cucumbers, and squash. If they can reach it, they will either eat it or ruin it. The solution is to fence the garden with 48-inch poultry netting with a strand of barbed wire six inches above that. Initial costs of fencing are high, but this fence will also keep out rabbits, turtles, dogs, and other small animals that can't climb. Depending on climate, poultry netting will last for eight to twelve years before it rusts away.

My garden fence worked beautifully at keeping the hens out until I bought several dozen Barred Rocks. They were apparently the hoodlums of the chicken world, because they gleefully sailed over the fence and made confetti out of my vegetable plants. If you keep big heavy birds that don't fly well, a garden fence may be all that is required. But now I routinely clip the flight feathers of my birds.

Clipping a hen's wing feathers is easy and it doesn't hurt the bird. Use a large pair of scissors or pruning shears to cut the feathers. Wear long pants and a long-sleeved shirt to help prevent being clawed by a struggling bird. Grasp the chicken around the body for a moment to calm her. If your birds are used to being handled, you may be able to squat on the ground and have the bird stand next to you during the clipping. For more skittish birds, stand upright and hold the hen's legs between your own knees. Cradle the hen's chest in the crook of your non-dominant arm and use that hand to spread the flight feathers out. Cut across the base of the long flight feathers, being careful not to cut the bird's skin.

I usually clip the feathers on only one wing. This allows medium-sized birds to gain a few feet of altitude to escape dogs and other small predators, but not enough to fly over a 4½-foot fence. Occasionally, I have to clip the feathers on both wings if it's a determined hen. Hens who repeatedly find a way into the garden end up as chicken soup. Chickens molt in late summer or fall, so the flight feathers must be trimmed again once they grow new ones.

Instead of trying to keep birds out of flower beds, try growing chicken-resistant flowers. Rose bushes and flowering shrubs are largely ignored by chickens. Irises, mums, and other tall plants are fairly resistant if they are protected when young. I place softball-sized rocks throughout the flower beds to prevent poultry from scratching and damaging plants' root systems. Chickens like to eat pansies, petunias, and impatiens, so I grow these favorites in hanging baskets on the porch.

Dealing with predators

Losing chickens to predators is another concern for owners of free-range birds. Foxes, coyotes, skunks, weasels, raccoons, opossums, and hawks all enjoy chicken for dinner. In the years I have owned poultry, I have lost perhaps 30 birds to predators. I can honestly say that 98% of the time the predator was my own dog. On two separate occasions, I took in stray dogs that turned out to be chicken-killers. It is probably a mistake to keep strays, or to accept "secondhand" or "free-to-a-good-home" dogs. Any canine not raised around free-roaming birds will likely become a chicken killer. Once they know it's wrong, they can be quite sneaky at it. Conversely, the best defense against other four-legged predators is a big farm dog patrolling his domain for interlopers. Our dogs consider themselves to be masters of all they survey. Several opossums and skunks have experienced an untimely demise because of my dogs' vigilance.

I don't have a serious problem with hawks. Only twice have I witnessed birds of prey

Demonstrating how to clip flight feathers on a very calm pullet

Spread the flight feathers and cut across their bases.

Be careful not to cut the skin.

Here's the finished wing.

attempting to take one of the hens. Once, a big red-tail plunged out of the sky, hit a hen in an explosion of feathers, but then left empty-taloned when the hen rolled under the tractor. The hen survived. Another time, some sort of falcon streaked between the barn and the coop and made a tight turn directly over the heads of several hens. They didn't wait for it to make a second pass, but dove for cover like kids playing commando. Suddenly aware that death could come from above, for weeks the flock was seldom seen out in the open. I raise dark-colored birds that blend in well with their surroundings. People I know who raise Buff Orpingtons or White Leghorns have more trouble with birds of prey. I suspect light-colored poultry make a more tempting target when viewed from the air. Seeing people up close makes hawks nervous, or perhaps they realize that their natural prey disappears when humans are around. So the best defense against birds of prey is a lot of outside human activity. A bunch of noisy rambunctious children works fabulously.

Where did the eggs go?

Another problem with free-ranging hens is the disappearance of eggs. Instead of using the nest boxes provided, chickens may prefer to find their own secret spots to lay eggs, often inconveniently located. The cure is to keep them in their coop until at least noon, to force them to lay where you want them to. Some will still delay egg laying until they're released. Every few days, we look in the spots where they have made secret nests in the past, and thus manage to collect most of the eggs.

Final thoughts

Keep in mind that anything harmful, such as pesticides, cleansers, or fertilizer, must be kept away from poultry. Chickens will eat things that other animals wouldn't dream of eating, and since they are in the human food chain, be especially vigilant. Poultry should not be allowed to forage in the trash, so keep trash and recycling bins covered and inaccessible. Besides the obvious poisoning opportunity, things like bits of aluminum foil or Styrofoam from cups or packing peanuts may stop up their crop and kill your flock.

A flock of hens parading around the farmstead is the image of country life. All these problems with free-ranging can be easily managed so that the farmstead can enjoy the benefits of less expensive birds and fewer insect pests.

BUTCHERING & RECIPES

Butchering chickens made easy

By Jackie Clay-Atkinson

Butchering chickens and other poultry is not my favorite homestead activity. But it is necessary, as we raise nearly all of our own meat. Through the years, we've developed an easy, fast, and stress-free way to get it done.

Preparing for butchering day

First off, let me say that because we have no enclosed butchering room or building, we choose to butcher our poultry outside during those cool fall and early winter days when the flies and other insects have gone for good.

The night before, we withhold all feed from the pen of meat birds we plan on butchering the next morning. It's a great help to gently corral the butcher birds into their own smaller coop or pen so there's less stress when you go to catch them. Although their feed is withheld to make their crop and intestinal tract relatively empty, we do give them plenty of fresh water.

Next, we assemble our butchering equipment in the form of a plastic table — stainless steel would be best but we don't have one, our now-famous Tornado Clucker Plucker (the tub-style chicken plucker that my husband, Will, built last year), an extension cord, a metal killing cone of appropriate size (we have three: one for smaller birds, one for meat birds, and a third for turkeys), a garbage can to rake the feathers into, and a small bucket to hold the heads, feet, and guts. We also pull a garden hose into place, attached to our frost-free hydrant by the driveway. I make sure I have a clean metal washtub ready to hold ice water (to cool the processed chickens in) and two or more sharp, medium-sized knives. Cutting through bone, as you will with the neck and legs, can quickly dull knives. If you're planning on butchering several chickens, have enough knives so you can switch knives as they become dull. Believe it or not, it's the dull knives that will get you cut! You have to put so much pressure on them that they easily slip and gouge your fingers.

It's always easier to work as a team. Folks at our homestead seminar learned how to hand-pluck and eviscerate chickens. Here, Deb is plucking a bird that has been scalded.

I also make sure I have a good supply of plastic wrap and freezer bags to hold the cleaned birds. Even with us living off grid, I usually freeze several birds during butchering season so that I can roast a few or make fried chicken.

Butchering day

We like to get everything set up before the first chickens are caught. We scrub the plastic table clean and rinse it with a bleach solution of about ¼ cup bleach to a gallon of water, then we rinse it off with clean water and allow the table to sun-dry. We haul out a galvanized washtub to fill later with ice-cold well water. I put a boiling water bath kettle on the stove about ⅔ full of water and turn it on to get hot. If we're doing more than three or four birds, I heat two kettles.

We plug in the Clucker Plucker and assemble our equipment. We hang the killing cone by a nail on a convenient tree. We like the cone much better than the old chop-the-head-off method. The birds don't struggle and don't flop about after death, which often causes bruising and broken wings.

I catch two birds and place them in a small dog carrier and then bring it up to Will. While he's killing the two birds, I go catch two more.

To kill the chickens, Will holds the head down, neck extended, in the killing cone and cuts beneath the head with a very sharp knife, first on one side of the neck, then the other, severing the jugular vein. The birds bleed out and die very quickly with little muscular spasming.

While Will is killing the last chickens, I go into the house and bring out the canning kettle full of boiling water. We use a thermometer to ensure that the temperature of the water is between 145 to 150° F. Too cool of water and the birds' feathers won't come out. Too hot of water and the skin will begin to cook and will tear easily.

We hold the dead bird by the feet, immerse it in the hot water, plunging it down so that all of the feathers are covered with the hot water. We leave it in for about 3-4 seconds, then pull it out and again plunge it in, kind of swishing it up and down to make sure that the feathers aren't preventing the hot water from getting to the skin. We then pull the bird out of the water and test our scald by trying to pull out a wing and tail feather. If the feathers slip out without much effort, we know our scald is perfect. If not, we dunk it again, each time for a few seconds only.

The old way of simply dunking the bird in once, using a water temperature of between 135-140° F and holding it in for 30 seconds, sometimes caused the muscle to harden, resulting in tougher birds. We like the "double-dunk" method better.

We scald two birds at a time so that we can then toss them "hot" into the Clucker Plucker. Will turns it on and holds the hose ready to flush the feathers out while I gently drop the birds into the plucker. In 10 seconds, we have two cleanly-plucked chickens!

We didn't always have our wonderful Clucker Plucker; in the past we'd place two hot scalded chickens on the table and hand-pluck them. If they were scalded right, the feathers would slip right out by the handfuls. I tossed them into a garbage bag-lined can so cleanup was easier after butchering. After all the main feathers were off, I would go over the chickens with a paring knife and my thumbnail to remove any pinfeathers.

After plucking, we rinse the chickens off with the hose, turn off the water, and begin eviscerating.

Eviscerating

I've found that eviscerating is easier if you don't save the tail. So after I cut off the head (usually with a larger butcher knife to save my smaller knife's sharpness), I also remove the legs by bending them *very* straight and cutting down through the joint. You want to cut the leg apart at the joint, not through the bone. With a bit of experience, this is very easy to do. I then remove any clinging scales on the leg joint.

Turning the bird on its breast, I cut through the tail, close to the body, *not* cutting through the muscle and skin by the rectum.

Then I keep the bird on its breast and cut the skin along the neck, down to the body. I pull

Our friend, Jeri, demonstrates scalding chickens at one of our homestead seminars.

Two chickens after 8 seconds in Will's Tornado Clucker Plucker

the skin away from the neck and body so I can find the crop, which is down lower next to the body. I get hold of the crop and cut it free, pulling it and the windpipe out.

Now I turn the bird over on its back and with one hand, pull up on the skin next to the breastbone and begin cutting gently there. I don't want to cut deeply, just through the skin and muscle until I've opened the abdominal cavity. I keep cutting on each side, down along the ribs and around and beneath the vent, using my fingers as a guide to hold the skin and muscle up so I don't cut through the intestines.

At this point, I cut down and remove the tail. I reach deep inside the bird with my cupped hand and pull out the entire mass of internal organs. Sometimes this requires a little strength, depending on the size and age of the

After 10 seconds in the plucker, the chicken is completely naked.

bird. Usually the organs will slide right out in one mass.

You can either dispose of the entire viscera in a bucket or you can search through it for the giblets: the liver, gizzard, and heart. The liver is relished by many. Just don't break the gallbladder, the small greenish "sack" attached to it. Carefully cut it free, not squeezing on it. The heart only requires rinsing well. The gizzard is where the bird grinds its food so you'll need to carefully cut into the large end until you reach the tough lining. Then carefully peel it away. You can chop the gizzard up to use in various recipes.

Back inside the carcass, I scrape out the lungs and testicles (if it's a rooster). These are usually attached to the inside of the ribs. I just use my fingernails and scrape them out. You can choose to use a tablespoon with the handle cut off instead. This works quite well.

I reach way up into the body cavity and grasp the esophagus, which feels like a tough, limber straw, and pull it firmly out. Sometimes you have to wind it around your finger to get a good enough grip on it.

Now I rinse the bird very well with cold running water and drop it into the washtub full of cold water to start chilling.

I repeat this process until all birds have been done. After three or four birds, the scalding water will become too cool for good scalding, so I either bring out another hot kettle or reheat to a proper temperature with fresh water.

Once all of the birds have been done, I remove them one at a time from the chilling water, pat them dry with a clean towel, and hold them by the legs with one hand while I move a propane torch lightly over the body to singe off any hairs.

I then take the finished birds in to the kitchen sink which I've filled with cold water (I have a large, deep sink). I hold the birds in this cold water until their body heat has left, often refilling the sink several times to keep the water cold. Then I dry them carefully and put them loosely in plastic bags and refrigerate for 24 hours. *All* chickens should be placed in the refrigerator for at least 24 hours to chill — even the ones meant for the freezer. This will keep them from getting tough.

Once thoroughly chilled, I wrap the chickens tightly in plastic wrap and place them in freezer bags, removing as much air as possible.

Of course, any birds you want to eat right away don't have to be double-wrapped and can be cooked as soon as you wish after being chilled for 24 hours.

Although butchering is not fun, just think of all of that great eating on the days and weeks following it. Home-raised chicken tastes *so* much better than anything you can buy in the stores. And once you've gotten the hang of it, the whole process can be accomplished quickly and easily.

Chicken dishes eaten along the Silk Road and beyond

By Habeeb Salloum

As a young boy, one of the many things that I remember about our kitchen is the variety of chicken dishes that my mother made. Wholesome and hearty, they helped us survive the Depression years on southern Saskatchewan's prairies. Our chickens were not the pampered and cooped-up types that we devour today. Instead, they survived by finding their own food in the barnyard and nearby fields. Our family ate my mother's Middle Eastern chicken dishes from chickens stuffed with burghul or rice, to the many *yakhnees* (stews) and soups that came out of her kitchen. The soups we ate when we children were sick with colds and the flu helped us overcome these sicknesses. Chicken was an important part of our meals when we grew up and it seemed the dishes my mother prepared with this poultry were endless, each more flavorful than the next.

Chicken, known for centuries as the meat of the poor, served us well throughout these years of hardship. Chicken meat is packed with vitamins and nutrients. It is versatile and an excellent source of protein — a healthy alternative to red meat. It has been found that chicken soup is valid even in our modern age; it helps relieve a cold.

Starting at the Pacific Ocean, then crossing China and Central Asia, a traveler comes to Western Asia and the Mediterranean and along this route meets up with a variety of unique tastes and flavors. To travel the Silk Route, one need only venture into these varieties of chicken dishes to relish what makes each unique with their additions of aromatic spices and sauces.

Chicken casserole

Chicken casserole — *Adobong manok*

Serves about 6

Considered to be the Philippines' national dish, this Spanish-influenced dish is simple to prepare.

4 Tbsp. cooking oil
1 chicken (about 4 lbs.), cut into serving-sized pieces
1 garlic head, peeled and crushed
½ cup white vinegar
5 Tbsp. soy sauce
1½ tsp. black pepper
6 bay leaves
¼ cup water

Heat oil in a saucepan, then fry chicken and garlic over medium-low heat for 10 minutes, turning chicken pieces over once. Add remaining ingredients and bring to boil, then cover and cook over medium-low heat for 40 minutes or until chicken is well done, turning over chicken pieces once and adding a little water if necessary. Drizzle the sauce over the chicken pieces and serve over cooked rice.

Malaysian chicken fried rice

Chicken with lemongrass

Chicken meatballs

Malaysian chicken fried rice — *Nasi goreng*

Serves about 6

This is my own version of this dish — a famous Malay Archipelago treat.

4 Tbsp. cooking oil
½ lb. boneless chicken, cut into ½-inch cubes
1 medium onion, finely chopped
2 garlic cloves, crushed
½ lb. cooked shrimp
1 cup fresh or frozen green peas
¾ tsp. salt
½ tsp. black pepper
tsp. cayenne pepper
2 cups cooked medium or long grain white rice
6 eggs
4 Tbsp. shredded lettuce leaves
a handful of fresh cilantro
½ small tomato, quartered and thinly sliced

Heat oil in saucepan and sauté chicken over medium heat for 5 minutes. Add onion and garlic, then sauté for a further 8 minutes. Stir in shrimp, green peas, salt, pepper, and cayenne pepper, then stir-fry for another 5 minutes. Stir in rice and stir-fry for a few minutes, then place on a platter.

Fry eggs over easy then place evenly on top. Garnish with lettuce, cilantro, and tomato, then serve as-is or with peanut sauce.

Chicken with lemongrass — *Ga xao xa ot*

Serves 4 to 6

Spicy and tasty, this Vietnamese dish is simple to prepare.

Nuoc Mam is a type of fish sauce that is available in any Asian market.

4 Tbsp. vegetable oil
2 medium onions, thinly sliced
4 garlic cloves, thinly sliced
2 Tbsp. finely-chopped lemongrass
1 fresh small chile pepper, seeded and finely chopped
2 lbs. boneless chicken breast, cut into ½-inch cubes
½ tsp. salt
3 Tbsp. Nuoc Mam
1 Tbsp. sugar
2 cups water

In frying pan, heat oil over medium heat. Add onion and garlic, then stir-fry for 3 minutes. Add lemongrass and chile, then stir-fry for a further 2 minutes. Stir in chicken and fry for another 5 minutes, stirring often. Add remaining ingredients, then cover and simmer over low heat for 40 minutes or until chicken becomes tender, stirring often. Add more water if necessary. Serve hot.

Chicken meatballs — *Tsukune*

Serves 4 to 6

A Japanese dish, these meatballs make an excellent appetizer. Shoyu, a type of Japanese soy sauce, and Mirin, a variety of sweet rice wine, are available at most Asian grocery outlets or markets.

1 lb. ground chicken
½ cup finely chopped mushrooms
½ cup fine bread crumbs
¼ cup finely chopped onion
1 egg, beaten
1 Tbsp. finely grated fresh ginger
1 Tbsp. Shoyu
1 Tbsp. mirin
½ tsp. salt
vegetable oil for frying

Korean chicken soup

Combine all ingredients except oil. Form mixture into small balls and set aside. Pour oil to about ¾-inch deep in a frying pan, then fry balls over medium heat until they brown. Serve hot.

Korean chicken soup

Serves 6 to 8

This tasty dish can be served along with a sandwich for a filling lunch.

8 cups chicken broth
6 cloves garlic, crushed
2 Tbsp. grated fresh ginger
½ cup medium grain white rice, rinsed
4 Tbsp. soy sauce
tsp. cayenne pepper
2 cups shredded cooked chicken
½ cup finely chopped green onion
1 Tbsp. sesame seeds, lightly toasted

Place chicken broth, garlic, ginger, and rice in a large saucepan, then bring to boil. Cover and cook over medium-low heat for 15 minutes. Add soy sauce, cayenne pepper, and chicken, then re-cover and cook for a further 5 minutes.

Pour soup into bowls. Garnish with green onion and sesame seeds and serve hot.

Beijing five-spice chicken

Serves about 4

This dish is very simple to prepare.

4 Tbsp. Chinese stir-fry sauce
4 cloves garlic, crushed
½ tsp. salt
¼ tsp. cinnamon
¼ tsp. ground cloves
¼ tsp. ground fennel seed
¼ tsp. ground aniseed
¼ tsp. chili flakes
3 Tbsp. sesame oil
2 lbs. chicken wings or legs

Combine sauce, garlic, salt, the five spices, and oil, then coat chicken wings or legs and marinate for 4 hours.

Preheat the oven to 350° F. Place chicken wings or legs (with their marinade juice) side by side in a greased casserole dish. Cover and bake for 40 minutes. Uncover, then turn over

Beijing five-spice chicken

Cantonese almond chicken

Chicken pakodas

and bake for another 30 minutes. Serve with cooked rice and the juices from the casserole.

Cantonese almond chicken

Serves about 6

I have dined on different versions of this dish for years, yet I still look forward to it anytime.

Sauce

1 Tbsp. cornstarch, dissolved in 2 Tbsp. water
2 Tbsp. soy sauce
½ cup chicken broth
¼ cup white grape juice
2 tsp. sugar

Combine all the sauce ingredients in a small bowl and set aside.

1 lb. chicken breast, cut into ½-inch cubes
4 Tbsp. thinly sliced leeks
2 cloves garlic, crushed
1 tsp. grated fresh ginger
3 Tbsp. soy sauce
4 Tbsp. peanut or olive oil
1 cup water chestnuts, drained and sliced
1 cup sliced mushrooms
2 cups snow peas, cut into about ½-inch pieces
½ cup lightly-toasted almonds

In a bowl, place chicken, leeks, garlic, ginger, and soy sauce and allow to marinate for 30 minutes.

Heat oil in a wok or heavy frying pan, then stir-fry chicken with its marinade over medium-high heat for 4 minutes. Stir in water chestnuts, mushrooms, and snow peas, then stir-fry for another 3 minutes. Stir in sauce then stir-fry for 3 more minutes.

Place on a serving platter, spread almonds over top, and serve hot with cooked rice or noodles.

Chicken pakodas

Serves 6 to 8

This Indian dish from Hyderabad is also found in the Arab countries along the Persian Gulf — no doubt taken there by the thousands of Indian workers in the petroleum industry.

Chicken and yogurt

1 lb. chicken, cut into small pieces
2 eggs, beaten
1 cup flour
4 tsp. cornstarch
1 medium onion, finely chopped
½ cup fresh coriander leaves, chopped
½ cup fresh mint leaves, chopped
1 Tbsp. lemon juice
1 Tbsp. hot chili sauce
1 Tbsp. grated fresh ginger
2 tsp. garlic powder
1 tsp. turmeric
1 tsp. salt
oil for deep-frying

Place chicken in saucepan and cover with water, then bring to boil. Cook for 1 hour over medium heat, then drain and allow to cool (reserve 1½ cups of the water).

Transfer chicken to a food processor then add all other ingredients, except oil, and process for 2 minutes. Transfer to a mixing bowl, then add enough of the reserved water to make a thick batter of dropping consistency, adding more water or flour if necessary.

Heat oil to medium in a saucepan then drop in heaping tablespoons of batter. Remove when pakodas turn golden brown and drain on paper towels. Serve with chutney or tomato ketchup.

Chicken and yogurt — *Dajaj bil laban*

Serves about 4

This dish originating in the Persian Gulf region of the Arabian Peninsula is popular in that part of the world. The combined taste of yogurt and chicken is exotic and unique.

- 6 Tbsp. olive oil
- 2 medium onions, finely chopped
- 4 cloves garlic crushed
- 2 lbs. skinless, boneless chicken breast, cut into 1-inch cubes
- 1 small hot pepper, seeded and finely chopped
- 1 tsp. salt
- 1 tsp. ground coriander
- 1 tsp. freshly ground black pepper
- 1½ cups water
- 1 cup yogurt, mixed with ¼ cup water, 1 tsp. dried mint and ¼ tsp. salt

Heat oil in a saucepan, then fry onions over medium-low heat for 10 minutes. Add garlic, chicken, and hot pepper, and stir-fry for 5 minutes. Stir in the 1 teaspoon salt, coriander, pepper, and water. Cover and cook over low heat for 50 minutes or until chicken is done, stirring occasionally and adding more water if necessary.

Place yogurt in another saucepan and bring to a boil, stirring constantly in one direction. Remove from heat and add to the chicken. Cover and continue to simmer over low heat for 10 minutes, stirring often. Serve with rice.

Chicken with sumac — *Musakhkhan*

Serves about 6

One of the greatest chicken meals that I ever enjoyed was *musakhkhan* in the village of Kalkiliya in Palestine. A Palestinian friend of ours in Canada, after having learned that we would be touring the West Bank, urged us to visit his family in his hometown. The first night we arrived, his mother prepared a feast arranged around a massive platter of musakhkhan. The dish, oozing with oil, onions, pine nuts, sumac, thin crispy layers of bread and, of course, chicken, was a royal feast fit for any caliph.

Musakhkhan should be always be served with yogurt and a tomato and cucumber salad.

Chicken with sumac

1 medium-sized chicken (3 to 4 lbs.), cleaned and cut into serving pieces
6 cardamom seeds, crushed and divided
¾ cup cooking oil, divided
4 large onions, thinly sliced
1 tsp. salt
½ tsp. black pepper
½ tsp. allspice
¼ cup pine nuts
½ cup sumac
4 small loaves Arab bread (pita)

In a pot, place chicken pieces and half of crushed cardamom seeds, then cover with water. Cover and cook over medium heat until chicken is tender, then remove chicken pieces and set aside.

In the meantime, in a saucepan, place ½ cup of the oil, onions, salt, pepper, allspice, and the remaining cardamom, then simmer uncovered over low heat for about 30 minutes or until onions turn golden brown.

While onions are simmering, sauté pine nuts in remaining ¼ cup of oil until they begin to brown, then add with sumac to the onions. Stir and allow to cool.

Preheat oven to 350° F. Split open bread loaves, then arrange them in a greased, round, deep casserole, spreading a portion of onion/sumac mixture on each piece of bread. (Use about ½ of the mixture.) Top evenly with the chicken pieces, then spread remaining half of the onion/sumac mixture over the chicken. Cover with thick brown paper and bake for 40 minutes, then while hot, serve a portion of the bread with each chicken piece.

Make your own charcuterie from geese and ducks

By Amanda J. Kemp

When people hear that my family only eats wild game, they come to one of two assumptions. Either they picture us being one step above Neanderthals, huddled around a fire in a dank cave, or they picture us drowning meat in barbeque sauce. The truth is, we eat better than anyone else I know.

Even though I would argue that comfort foods made with wild game (like venison shepherd's pie or squirrel dumplings) are some life's finer pleasures, I do create more haute cuisine with some of the game my husband brings home. Specifically, I use charcuterie methods on geese and ducks.

Charcuterie is essentially a fancy term for preserving meats via salting, smoking, or cooking. Though these methods are slow, they are quite easy to do. The results are amazing, elevating a humble bird into a sublime dining experience. It is believed that the development of the ability to preserve meat allowed early people to turn from a nomadic existence to one of more permanence. There is some dispute as to how charcuterie methods were discovered. One theory is that meat was hung near the fire overnight so as to dissuade bugs and animals, while another theory contends that people ate animals that had been killed in forest fires.

In either case, apparently, it's so easy a caveman could do it. I, myself, have used these techniques with wild ducks and geese, though domestic can be used.

Prosciutto

Prosciutto is a form of dry curing that utilizes salt to preserve the meat. It's dry in that the salt is directly applied to the flesh, as opposed to brining, when the salt is first dissolved in water. This recipe will create a flavorful meat that is best sliced thinly. Serve the slices over mixed greens or with pieces of melon. In my house, we put it on crackers with cheese.

2 cups salt (maybe more)
1 whole breast of a duck or goose
½ tsp. pepper
cheesecloth

The first step is to remove the breasts from the carcass. Make sure your knife is sharp enough to slide through skin, which on a wild duck or goose is surprisingly tough and rubbery. Likely, you will need to sharpen your knife during the process. I found it easier to follow along the rib cage and then cut along the sternum to free the cut of meat.

Take the breasts, now free of the carcass, and place them in a container just large enough to hold the pieces so that they don't touch. You don't want a container larger than it needs to be, to avoid using more salt than necessary. Cover the bottom of the container with salt. Then, place the meat on top, making sure that the meat is not touching. Finally, cover the meat completely with the salt. Place a cover on the container; plastic wrap is fine if you don't have a lid to match the container you chose. Leave the meat for 24 hours in the refrigerator.

Remove the meat from the salt, which will be tinged pink from the blood. Do not be alarmed; it's completely normal. Thoroughly rinse the meat, now a darker color and dense in texture, and pat dry. You can dust the meat with pepper, if you like.

Wrap the breast in cheesecloth (I used a fabric remnant with a loose weave, rather than purchase cheesecloth) and tie with string. Hang the meat in a cool, humid place about 50-60° F for about seven days. I hung mine in my refrigerator and hoped for the best. In order

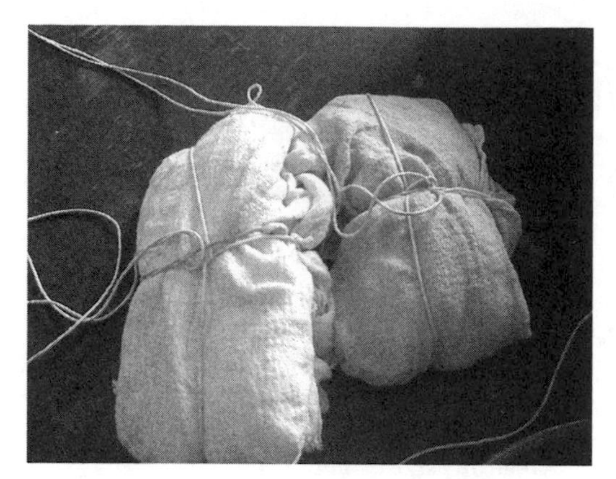

The wrapped goose breasts will make delicious prosciutto in 7-18 days.

to hang the meat, I took a large pot and laid a spoon across the top. I hung the meat from the spoon handle, thus allowing the meat to age. After seven days, check the meat for completion. The flesh should be stiff but not entirely hard, and the color should be much darker. If it still feels raw in the center, hang for longer. I found that mine took two and half weeks until it was done. Once it's done, cover in plastic wrap and refrigerate until you're ready to use it. It will keep for several weeks.

Confit

Many hunters merely remove the breast from a goose or duck, leaving the rest of the carcass for scavengers. This is an appalling waste when there are so many delicious recipes that could use the rest of the bird.

Confit is a succulent way to make use of the often discarded legs of wild fowl. Just remove the legs at the joint and put in the freezer until you have enough collected to make confit. Literally, the word "confit" translates to "preserved." Confit can be made from many cuts of meat. Duck is most common, though it can be made from goose, chicken, turkey, or pork loin. The meat is salted for hours or even days, then poached in its own fat. Finally, it is submerged in the fat and allowed to age, developing an even deeper flavor. It is stored in the fat until it's ready to be heated and served.

Confit makes for an elegant meal when served with potatoes and a glass of wine.

6 duck or goose legs (enough to make roughly five pounds. If using wild ducks, you'll require far more than six legs)
3 Tbsp. salt
3 garlic cloves, sliced
3 bay leaves
cracked pepper
2-4 cups duck or goose fat, lard, or some combination thereof (I used fat that I saved from another goose that I roasted)

Sprinkle the legs all over with the salt, placing them in a plastic or glass container. This is to avoid an off-flavor developing from a reaction between salt and certain metals. Scatter some pepper evenly over the meat, but not too thickly. Then, press the sliced garlic onto the flesh of each leg. Break up the bay leaves, distributing them evenly across the legs. Cover them with plastic wrap and refrigerate overnight to as long as 48 hours.

Under cold water, rinse the duck legs and remove all the seasonings. Pat them dry with a paper towel or lint free cloth. Preheat the oven to 180-200° F (the lowest your oven will go within this range).

Place the duck legs in an oven-safe, six-quart pot (a Dutch oven works well). Cover them with fat completely, then heat the pot to a simmer over medium-high heat. Place the uncovered pot into the oven and cook for six to ten hours. You will know they are done when they are resting on the bottom of the pot and the meat is tender.

Cool the legs to room temperature, then refrigerate, making sure that the legs are submerged in fat, as the fat is what preserves them. Store in the refrigerator for up to a month. I get so excited to eat it that I am usually only able to restrain myself for a week.

Remove from the refrigerator several hours before you wish to serve it. If you skip this step, the skin will tear when you try to remove the legs from the fat that is still hard and cold. Put the legs on a baking sheet, and roast them until the skin is crispy, about 15 to 20 minutes.

The fat left over from the process can be reused several times, or it can be used for frying potatoes. The meat left from confit can be turned into rillettes. Of course, the confit is so delicious, you'll have to put the meat aside for rillettes before you serve the confit. Otherwise, there won't be anything left.

Rillettes

Rillettes are a fine addition to any party as an hors d'oeuvre or just a decadent indulgence for yourself. Rillettes are a preparation of meat that is first pounded to a spreadable paste, then covered with a layer of fat. They can be kept in the refrigerator for a month or longer. Well-wrapped, they will keep in the freezer for three months. Confit meat makes for the best rillettes, because it has been cooked in flavorful fat rather than broth.

½ lb. confit meat
¼ cup fat from confit
¼ cup confit jelly (the gelatinous mass that develops on the bottom of the confit after it's been refrigerated — it sounds gross, but tastes great)
freshly ground black pepper
salt, if needed (I didn't find that it was needed)

Tear or chop the meat into very small pieces. With a mixer, blend in the fat and confit jelly, seasoning it with pepper, to taste. Mix on high until the fat is evenly distributed, the meat dispersed, and the whole concoction creamy in

Leftover confit makes the best rillettes.

appearance. The consistency should be quite spreadable; if it's too stiff, add more fat and/ or jelly.

Transfer to a smaller container and refrigerate. Once it's cooled, you can seal it with a layer of fat or Dijon mustard. Serve on toasted baguettes or crackers.

Further reading

My recipes were inspired by the book *Charcuterie: The Craft of Salting, Smoking, and Curing* by Michael Ruhlman and Brian Polcyn. This would be an excellent addition to your cookbook library. The recipes range from salt curing and smoked sausage to *pâtés*. Not only does the book include recipes, but it also explains the reason for the instructions, allowing the reader to better understand the process. Since many of these recipes are not in the average American diet, I particularly appreciate that it gives tips on how to serve the food as well.

Another terrific resource is the website honest-food.net by Hank Shaw. Not only is he a dedicated foodie, but he is also an avid hunter. His recipes are tailored specifically for wild game. The website offers a plethora of recipes and articles; his humorous tone is an added bonus.

With only a small investment of actual hands-on time, you will be amazed at the delectable treats that you have created. You may even find yourself thumbing through recipes, looking for the next level in charcuterie. A venison salami, anyone?

Squab recipes

By Allen Easterly

Usually considered a delicacy, squab is tender, moist, and richer in taste than many commonly-consumed poultry meats. The majority of the meat lies in the breast. Squab is an all dark-meat bird. The skin is fatty like that of a duck, but the meat is lean, easily digestible, and rich in proteins, minerals, and vitamins. It is often described as having a silky texture and is very tender and fine-grained. Squab's flavor lends itself to complex red or white wines. The birds are suitable for roasting, grilling, or searing. The adult birds are tougher than that of young squab and are best prepared in casseroles or slow-cooked stews.

Squab nutritional information (3.5 oz., raw)

Calories 142
Total fat 8g
Saturated fat 2g
Cholesterol 90mg
Sodium 51mg
Carbohydrates 0g
Dietary Fiber 0g
Sugars 0g
Protein 18g

The following are recipes I've collected over the years from various sources. They are all good and I use them regularly.

Roast squab with bacon & grapes

1 stick unsalted butter, softened
2 Tbsp. juniper berries, crushed
salt and freshly ground pepper
vegetable oil, for frying
8 squabs
8 slices of bacon, halved
3 cups red or green seedless grapes

Preheat the oven to 450° F. In a small bowl, blend the butter with the juniper and season with salt and pepper.

In a large skillet, heat ¼ inch of vegetable oil until shimmering. Season the squabs with salt and pepper. Add four of the squabs to the skillet, breast-side down, and cook over moderately high heat, turning a few times, until richly browned all over, about 12 minutes. Repeat with the remaining squab, adding more oil to the skillet as needed.

Arrange the squabs breast-side up on a large, rimmed baking sheet. Rub the squab cavities with the juniper butter. Arrange two bacon halves on each squab breast in a single layer. Scatter the grapes around the squab and roast in the upper third of the oven for about 15 minutes, until an instant-read thermometer inserted in the thickest part of the legs registers 125° F for medium-rare meat. Transfer the squab to a carving board and let rest for about 5 minutes.

Using a large knife, cut each squab in half, cutting through the breast bone. Transfer the squabs to plates. Spoon the grapes and roasting juices on top and serve.

Rice-stuffed squab

1 cup chopped celery
½ cup chopped onion
3 Tbsp. butter
1½ cups cooked rice
1½ cups chopped fresh mushrooms
⅓ to ½ cup raisins
6 Tbsp. orange juice concentrate, divided
1 Tbsp. minced fresh parsley
1½ tsp. salt, divided
¾ tsp. dried marjoram
6 dressed squab (about 1 lb. each)
¾ cup canola oil

In a large skillet, sauté celery and onion in butter until tender. Add the rice, mushrooms, raisins, 3 tablespoons of the orange juice concentrate, parsley, half the salt, and marjoram. Sprinkle cavities of squab lightly with remaining salt; stuff with rice mixture.

Place on a rack in a roasting pan. Combine oil and remaining orange juice concentrate; drizzle over squab. Bake uncovered, basting frequently, at 375° F for 1 hour or until meat juices run clear and a meat thermometer inserted into the stuffing reads 165° F. Yields six servings.

Picture courtesy of rendezvoushobbyfarm.com.

Simple roast squab

1⅓ sticks unsalted butter, softened and divided
2 large shallots, minced
2 Tbsp. fresh thyme leaves, chopped
zest of 1 lemon, finely grated
½ tsp. sea salt
freshly-ground pepper
1 tsp. kosher salt or coarse sea salt
4 squabs, rinsed and dried
3 Tbsp. olive oil

Preheat oven to 450° F. In a mixing bowl, beat together 1 stick of butter, shallots, thyme leaves, lemon zest, sea salt, and several grinds of freshly ground pepper until smooth. Divide into four portions.

Using a couple of fingers, carefully loosen each squab's skin attached to the breast and legs, then work in one portion of the butter mixture, spreading it over the breast meat and in between the legs. Stuff the squab's cavity with a thyme sprig and tie its legs together with kitchen string. Sprinkle kosher salt and more pepper over the squab. Repeat with the others.

Heat the remaining butter and olive oil in a heavy skillet over medium-high heat until the foam subsides. Place the squab in the skillet, brown on all sides, then transfer to a roasting pan. Roast for 15-20 minutes. Use an instant-read thermometer to check the internal temperature of the breast without touching bone. At 145° F, remove the squab from the oven and let rest 5 minutes before serving. (If the temperature is not at 145° F, continue to roast five more minutes.)

Garlic & ginger grilled squab

4 squab
3 Tbsp. vegetable oil
1 Tbsp. finely-grated ginger
2 large garlic cloves, minced
1½ tsp salt, divided
1½ tsp black pepper
1 medium onion, thinly sliced
1 small cucumber, thinly sliced
1 medium carrot, thinly sliced
2 tsp. sugar
1½ Tbsp. white wine vinegar

Rinse and dry squabs thoroughly; cut in half down the backbone and press out flat. Rub with a little oil. Mix ginger, garlic, half the salt, and pepper together and rub evenly over squab. Set aside for at least one hour.

Prepare a fire in the grill. Cook squab, brushing occasionally with remaining oil. Turn several times and cook until surface is golden-brown and meat feels firm when pressed.

Place vegetables in a dish. Mix remaining salt with sugar and vinegar and pour over vegetables. Knead squab meat with your fingers for a few minutes until softened, then arrange on warmed plates and garnish with vinegared vegetables.

Pinot noir glazed squab with roasted vegetables

1 cup olive oil
2 Tbsp. Dijon mustard
1 Tbsp. honey
1 cup pinot noir
four 1 lb. squabs, butterflied and breastbones removed
2 medium yellow squash, cut into 1-inch rounds
2 medium zucchini, cut into 1-inch rounds
1 lb. white mushrooms, stemmed
2 red bell peppers, cut into 1-inch pieces
1 red onion, halved and sliced lengthwise
2 tsp. finely-chopped thyme
1 tsp. finely-chopped sage
salt and freshly ground pepper
1 Tbsp. vegetable oil

In a medium bowl, combine the olive oil, mustard, and honey. In a small saucepan, boil the pinot noir until it is reduced to ¼ cup, about 7 minutes. Gradually whisk the hot wine into the marinade; let cool. Pour half of the marinade into a large, sturdy, resealable plastic bag and add the squabs. Let marinate, refrigerated, for two hours or overnight.

Preheat the oven to 425° F and position a rack in the upper third. In a large bowl, toss the vegetables and herbs with the remaining marinade and let stand for 15 minutes. Transfer to a large, rimmed baking sheet, season with salt and pepper, and roast for about 30 minutes, or until crisp-tender. Drain the vegetables in a colander for a few minutes, then return them to the baking sheet and roast for about five minutes more, or until tender. Transfer to a large platter, cover loosely, and keep warm.

Remove the squabs from the marinade and pat dry with paper towels. Heat the vegetable oil in a large, heavy skillet. Season the squabs with salt and pepper and add them to the skillet, skin side down. Cook over moderately high heat until the skin is dark brown, about three minutes. Transfer the squabs to a baking sheet, skin side up, and roast for 10 minutes for medium rare meat. Arrange the squabs on the vegetables and serve immediately.

Duck recipes

By Habeeb Salloum

Believed to have been domesticated in the Far East and still very popular in China, ducks are farmed for their meat, eggs, and down. They thrive in most environments, and are at home in cages, barns, or free on fields.

The breast and legs of ducks are the primary source of duck meat, which is darker than chicken or turkey meat. To some, the internal organs are considered delicacies and the liver is often substituted for goose liver in the famous *foie gras*.

Domesticated duck meat has a richer flavor than other fowl, and much more fat. Because of the high fat content, ducks are usually cooked at a higher temperature and for a longer time than chicken and low-fat meats.

The nutritional value of domestic duck is not widely known. Duck meat is a good source of quality protein and contains omega-6 fatty acids as well as generous amounts of iron, phosphorus, zinc, copper, selenium, thiamin, riboflavin, vitamin A, B6, B12, and traces of potassium and magnesium. In addition, duck meat contains fatty acids that cannot be produced by the body. When properly prepared and cooked, duck meat is not only tasty but nutritious.

Ducks are retailed as fresh or frozen whole ducks, breasts boned with or without skin, thighs, liver, and duck steaks — dried, smoked, and sliced.

During my travels and research, I have found that duck is used in a variety of dishes around the world. My favorite is often called the epitome of Chinese cuisine — Beijing duck.

Beijing duck

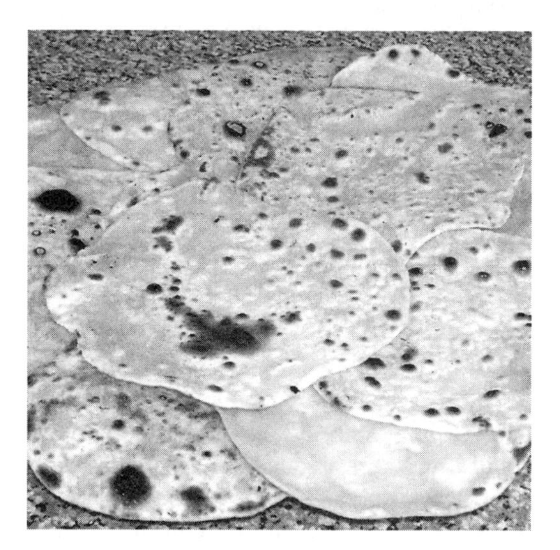

Chinese pancakes

Beijing duck

Serves about 6

Beijing duck is traditionally served in three courses: a soup made from the bones of the duck as the first course; duck pieces accompanied by pieces of crisp skin wrapped in Chinese pancakes with sliced shallots and hoisin sauce as the second course (in restaurants usually only this course is served); and finally, a stir-fry of the remaining pieces of the duck. Usually made for a minimum of six people, Beijing duck is prized, above all, for its crisp skin.

1 whole duck (about 4 to 6 lbs.), thoroughly cleaned
1 Tbsp. cinnamon
1 Tbsp. ground ginger
1½ tsp. ground black pepper
1 tsp. ground aniseed
½ cup liquid honey
2 Tbsp. light sesame oil
2 Tbsp. white vinegar
Chinese pancakes (recipe below)
1 small bunch green onions, cut in half lengthwise then cut into 2- to 3-inch pieces
Hoisin sauce

In a pot large enough to hold the duck, fill ¾ full of water, then bring to boil. Remove from heat then place duck in the boiling water for about 8 minutes. Remove duck and pat dry, then allow to stand for about 1 hour.

Place remaining ingredients, except green onions and hoisin sauce, in a saucepan. Bring to boil, then remove from heat and allow to cool.

Baste the duck all over, both inside and out, with the mixture, then allow to stand for 4 hours or until basting thoroughly dries on the duck.

Place duck, breast side up, in an oven preheated to 400° F. Roast for 30 minutes, then turn oven to 350° and roast for another 30 minutes. Turn duck over again and roast for 15 minutes, then turn again and roast for a further 15 minutes. During these last 30 minutes, you may want to turn the duck over more than twice to ensure that the skin browns evenly and gets crispy but does not burn. Serve duck pieces accompanied by pieces of the crispy skin wrapped in Chinese pancakes with sliced green onions and hoisin sauce.

Chinese pancakes

Beijing duck is always served in this pancake.

2 cups white flour
¾ cup warm water
2 Tbsp. light sesame oil

Knead flour and water into dough, then let stand for 1 hour. Form dough into 18 balls, then using a rolling pin, roll out into circles.

Duck stew

Roasted duck sandwich

Duck and chickpea salad

Duck and parsley salad

Brush the top of the circles with sesame oil. Place one circle over the second one with the pancakes' oiled surfaces touching. Roll each pair of circles into a thin, 5-inch circle. Heat a greased frying pan, then fry over medium-low heat 1 minute on each side. Remove and separate into two while hot then place on a platter. Cover to keep warm until ready to use.

Duck stew

Serves 6

My own version of a duck stew, this dish goes well with mashed potatoes.

4 Tbsp. cooking oil
½ lb. skinless duck breast, cut into ½-inch cubes
1 large onion, finely chopped
8 garlic cloves, crushed
½ cup finely-chopped fresh coriander leaves
2 medium carrots, peeled and sliced into thin rounds
3 cups chicken broth
4 cups water
2 cups stewed tomatoes
½ cup white rice
2 medium bell peppers, seeded and chopped
2 cups fresh or frozen peas
1 tsp. garam masala
1 tsp. salt
½ tsp. ground black pepper
½ tsp. dried rosemary
½ tsp. dried sage
⅛ tsp. cayenne pepper

Heat oil in a large saucepan, then sauté duck over medium heat for 8 minutes, stirring a few times. Add onion, garlic, and coriander, then stir-fry over medium-high heat for 3 minutes. Add carrots, chicken broth, and water, then bring to boil. Cover, turn to low, and cook for 1 hour. Stir in remaining ingredients and bring to boil. Turn heat to medium-low and cook for 40 minutes.

Roasted duck sandwich

Serves 6

2 Tbsp. butter
3 tsp. hoisin sauce
½ tsp. powdered mustard
½ tsp. dried basil
½ tsp. ground black pepper
½ tsp. salt
¼ tsp. chili powder
6 crusty buns, sliced sandwich style
1 lb. roasted duck, shredded
1 medium avocado, peeled and thinly sliced
2 medium tomatoes, thinly sliced into rounds
1 medium sweet Spanish onion, thinly sliced into rounds
Parmesan cheese, to taste

Thoroughly mix the butter, hoisin sauce, mustard, basil, pepper, salt, and chili powder. Lightly spread the mix evenly on the sliced buns and set aside.

Divide the duck, avocado, tomatoes, and onion into 6 equal parts then set aside.

Place on one side of the bun in that order — duck, avocado, tomatoes, and onion then sprinkle Parmesan cheese over the top to taste. Serve with soup for a light lunch.

Duck and chickpea salad

Serves 6

½ lb. cooked duck breast, cut into ½-inch cubes
2 cups cooked chickpeas
1 cup macaroni, cooked then cooled
½ cup pineapple, diced into ½-inch cubes
½ cup toasted slivered almonds
4 Tbsp. vinegar
4 Tbsp. olive oil
1 tsp. salt
½ tsp. ground black pepper
½ tsp. dry mustard

In a salad bowl, thoroughly combine duck, chickpeas, macaroni, pineapple, and almonds, then set aside.

To make the dressing, thoroughly mix the remaining ingredients then pour over the salad and gently stir. Refrigerate for 1 hour then toss and serve.

Duck and parsley salad

Serves 8

A unique way to dine on duck, this dish is healthy, tasty, and wholesome.

½ cup uncooked fine burghul, soaked for 10 minutes in warm water, then drained
4 cups finely-chopped parsley
1 cup finely-chopped fresh coriander leaves
½ cup finely-chopped mint leaves
½ cup finely-chopped green onions
1 medium cucumber, about 8 inches, quartered lengthwise and sliced into thin pieces
2 medium tomatoes, diced into ½-inch cubes
2 cups shredded, cooked duck meat
6 Tbsp. olive oil
6 Tbsp. lemon juice
1½ tsp. salt
½ tsp. ground black pepper
4 Tbsp. pomegranate seeds

Place all the ingredients, except the olive oil, lemon juice, salt, pepper, and pomegranate seeds, in a salad bowl and thoroughly mix. Set aside.

In a small bowl mix the olive oil, lemon juice, salt, and pepper, then stir into the ingredients in the salad bowl. Decorate with the pomegranate seeds and serve.

Duck and rice soup

Serves 8

Tasty and healthy, this soup will perk up the appetite for a light, yet filling, meal.

4 cups chicken broth
4 cups water
6 cloves garlic, crushed
2 Tbsp. grated fresh ginger
½ cup white rice
4 Tbsp. soy sauce
½ tsp. dried sage
⅛ tsp. cayenne pepper
2 cups cooked and shredded duck meat
½ cup finely-chopped green onions
2 Tbsp. finely chopped fresh coriander leaves

Place chicken broth, water, garlic, ginger, and rice in a large saucepan then bring to boil. Cover and cook over medium-low heat for 15 minutes. Add soy sauce, sage, cayenne, and duck. Re-cover and cook for a further 5 minutes.

Place soup into bowls, then garnish with green onions and coriander leaves and serve.

Duck and rice soup

Duck and pea stew

Duck and pea stew

Serves 6

4 Tbsp. cooking oil
2 lbs. duck legs
1 large onion, finely chopped
4 cloves garlic, crushed
½ cup finely-chopped fresh cilantro
1 small hot pepper, seeded and finely chopped
5 cups water
3 Tbsp. tomato paste dissolved in 1 cup water
1½ tsp. salt
1 tsp. garam masala
½ tsp. ground black pepper
½ tsp. cumin
½ tsp. sage powder
3 cups fresh or frozen peas
2 Tbsp. lemon juice

Heat oil in a saucepan over medium heat then fry duck over medium heat for 5 minutes, turning over once. Add onion, garlic, cilantro, and hot pepper then stir-fry for 3 minutes. Add water and bring to boil, then cover and cook over medium-low heat for 40 minutes. Stir in remaining ingredients except the lemon juice and bring to boil. Cook over medium-low heat for 30 minutes. Remove from heat and stir in lemon juice.

Serve hot with cooked rice.

Duck garlic casserole

Serves about 4

2 lbs. duck breast, cut into ½-inch cubes
2 Tbsp. tomato paste, diluted in 1 cup water
4 Tbsp. olive oil
1½ tsp. salt
1 tsp. ground black pepper
8 cloves garlic, crushed
½ tsp. dried sage
½ tsp. dried rosemary
⅛ tsp. cayenne

Combine all the ingredients in a casserole dish, then refrigerate and marinate for 1 hour. Cover and place in a preheated 300° F oven and bake for 2 hours or until duck is well-done. Serve hot from the casserole with cooked rice.

Grilled teriyaki duck

Serves 6

Wooden skewers should be used, soaked in water overnight to prevent them from burning during grilling.

6 Tbsp. soy sauce
4 Tbsp. olive oil
¼ cup dry wine
1 tsp. ground black pepper
2 Tbsp. fresh grated ginger
4 cloves garlic, crushed
2 skinless and boneless duck breasts, cut against grain into thin strips

Duck garlic casserole

Grilled teriyaki duck

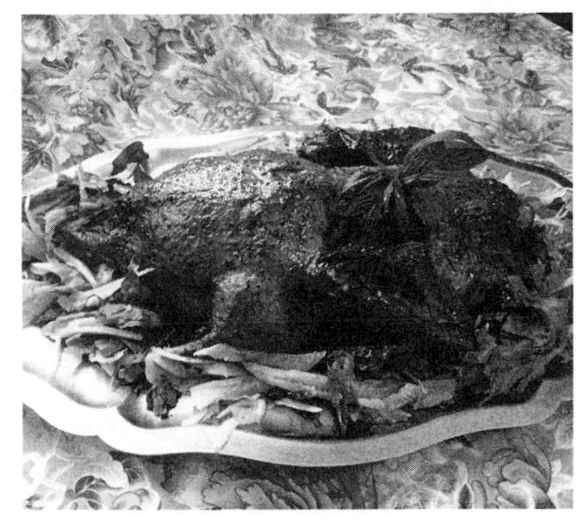

Orange-stuffed roast duck

In a bowl, combine soy sauce, oil, wine, pepper, ginger, and garlic. Gently stir in duck strips. Refrigerate and marinate some about 2 hours.

Place duck strips accordion style on skewers then grill for 3 minutes on each side, or until well done. Serve as an appetizer or with cooked rice as an entrée.

Orange-stuffed roast duck

Serves 4 to 6

The honey and oranges give the duck meat a sweet zesty taste that opens the appetite.

one 4-lb. whole duck, thoroughly washed
1 tsp. garlic powder
2 tsp. dried basil
1 tsp. nutmeg
1 tsp. ginger powder
1/2 tsp. dried rosemary
1/2 tsp. powdered sage
1/2 tsp. ground black pepper
1 /8 tsp. ground cloves
2 tsp. salt
4 Tbsp. lemon juice
3 small oranges, peeled and quartered
½ cup water
½ cup honey
¼ cup melted butter
½ cup undiluted orange juice

Preheat oven to 375° F.

In a small bowl, thoroughly mix the garlic, herbs, spices, salt, and lemon juice then rub the mixture on the inside and outside of the duck. Stuff duck with orange quarters and place on a rack in a roasting pan, breast up. Add water.

In a saucepan, combine the honey, butter, and orange juice. Simmer together over medium-low heat until the mixture turns syrupy. Pour a quarter of the mixture over the duck, saving the remainder for basting.

Cover the roasting pan and roast the duck for 30 minutes. Turn duck breast down, reduce heat to 325° F and roast covered for another 2 hours. Every 20 minutes, baste the meat with the remaining baste and the pan juices. Uncover the duck for the last 20 minutes of cooking. Remove from oven and allow to sit for 10 minutes before serving.

Canning chicken

By Jackie Clay-Atkinson

Chickens make the most economical meat possible on the homestead. With chickens, even a modest homestead can raise a whole lot of meat in a very small area. A small coop and run will help you raise all of the meat chickens that your family wants to eat. Or you can use a chicken tractor; a flock of meat birds can be moved daily to clean grass where they can scratch and run to their hearts' content.

You can freeze your home-butchered chicken, but after having one freezer full of food go bad due to a malfunction, I swore *that* would never happen again. So I switched from freezing my chicken to canning it. And by canning it, I quickly learned I could harvest many more meals per chicken than when I just froze it. Here are some basic canning directions for chicken, along with a bunch of tips on how to get more meals from your meat.

Basic instructions for canning chicken

Since chicken is a meat, it *must* be pressure canned. All low-acid foods, including vegetables, meats, and recipes including a mixture of both *must* be pressure canned in order to be eaten safely. To prevent the bacteria which causes botulism (a severe and potentially fatal form of food poisoning), foods must be processed under pressure at a temperature of 240° F for the recommended period of time. Botulism is not killed by processing in a water bath canner; no matter how long you process it, boiling food does not reach 240 degrees.

Once your chicken has been butchered, rinse it well with cold water, then chill in ice water for at least an hour. Drain and refrigerate in

My pantry shelves are full of canned chicken broth, chicken breasts, diced chicken, and chicken stew.

a plastic bag for 24 hours. This enables the chicken to become more tender. If you either cook or can the chicken immediately, before the body heat has completely left the bird, it will be tougher.

Always use extreme care to put cleanliness first during your butchering and handling of chickens.

After 24 hours have passed, remove the chickens from the refrigerator and rinse again. While it is possible to raw-pack chicken, I've found that it cans up much nicer if it is precooked at least enough that you can get the meat off of the bones. Uncooked, the meat slumps in the jars and looks unappetizing. When at least partially cooked, the meat retains its shape and the broth keeps it moist and tasty.

You can either cut up the chickens or cook them whole. I like to place the chicken(s) in a large stock pot and fill it with water, add salt and seasonings, and bring to a boil, covered. For a less hands-on approach, simply place two chickens side by side in a covered roasting pan and roast at 300° F until tender. When roasting, I add a quart of water during the last hour or so to ensure that the birds do not get dry.

Once cooked until tender, remove the pans from heat and let the birds cool until you can handle them without burning your fingers. Or, remove them from the broth if you've boiled them.

I sit at the table to bone the chicken. I use four bowls: one for diced meat, one for large pieces, one for bones, and another for "yucky" scraps like skin or gristle. I work with a cookie sheet under the area for easy clean-up. I fillet out the breast meat after pulling off the skin, then cut the breasts into large pieces. I cut up the rest of the chicken into bite-sized and smaller chunks. A very sharp paring knife is essential for quick and easy work.

Once the carcasses have been stripped of meat, they can be placed in a wire French fry basket and put back into the container the chicken was cooked in. If it was cooked in a turkey roasting pan, first scrape off and remove

Once chickens are butchered and cleaned, I take them into the house to hold in ice water for an hour. Chilling the carcasses before bagging and refrigerating them makes them more tender.

any clinging skin. Then add water, nearly to the top of the roaster once the wire basket with bones has been added.

Simmer the broth for 45 minutes or so to extract all flavor from the bones. (They *do* still have some clinging meat!) Remove the bones from the stock. I pour the stock through a wire sieve to remove any small bones or other unwanted debris. Taste and add seasonings as desired. I often add powdered chicken soup base to harvest more broth per chicken.

If you can't immediately begin packing and canning the chicken, cover the meat and refrigerate. Remember that all food tastes best when canned very soon after harvesting.

I've found that I really like to can up a lot of diced chicken in half-pint jars. This comes in handy for such recipes as casseroles that only use chicken as a "flavoring," not the main course. Otherwise, I can up my chicken in pints.

I always can up plenty of pints of chicken broth with pieces of meat. This makes a good base for many different recipes.

If you've refrigerated your chicken, it's a good idea to warm it before packing your jars. I do this by simply putting my aluminum foil-covered, stainless steel mixing bowls in the oven at 200° F until the meat is a little warmer than lukewarm.

Wash and rinse your canning jars, then leave them in a warm place. Carefully check each jar for any nicks in the rim of the jar or cracks. Discard any you find that are damaged.

Place your new jar lids in a pan of water and gently bring to a simmer. Keep the lids in warm water but do not boil. Directions on some brands of new lids say that they can be used successfully at room temperature, but I still like to soften them in hot water as I feel it will give a better seal.

I often pack the breast meat and other large chunks into pint jars, then cover the meat with broth. I add the smaller pieces sparingly to quart jars, and fill the rest of the jar with broth to make chicken soup base. Don't can it with noodles; add noodles when boiling the broth prior to eating.

Once the jars are filled as desired with meat, ladle boiling broth over the chicken, leaving an inch of headspace. You may use boiling water instead of broth, but the result is not as flavorful. If you use water, add ½ tsp. salt to each half-pint or pint and 1 tsp. to each quart to boost the flavor.

Once the jars are full, carefully wipe the rims of each jar with a clean, damp cloth to remove any bits of meat or grease. If you are using regular metal lids, put lids in place and screw down the rings firmly tight; do not over-tighten. Then place in the warmed canner. If you are using Tattler plastic reusable canning lids, place lids on jar and lightly finger-tighten the rings. *Do not* firmly tighten them! If you do, they will often not seal.

Place jars in canner and tighten the lid. Turn on the heat and exhaust canner. This means letting it heat until a steady stream of forceful steam comes from the petcock for 7-10 minutes. Then either place weight on petcock or flip it closed, depending on the style of canner. Always follow your canner's instruction manual.

Wait until the pressure climbs to 10 pounds, which is the pressure required if you live at an altitude below 1,000 feet. If you live at an altitude above 1,000 feet, consult your canning book for instructions on increasing your pressure to suit your altitude.

Once the pressure is correct, lower your heat to hold it at that pressure and begin timing. If your canner has a weight, begin timing when the weight begins to exhaust steam then lower the heat until the weight only rocks and spits about 2-4 times per minute. If you allow it to constantly spit steam and rock, it will lose too much steam and possibly run the canner dry.

Process half-pints and pints of chicken at 10 pounds pressure for 75 minutes and quarts for 90 minutes.

After processing, turn off the heat and let the canner's pressure return to zero. This usually takes 15 minutes or so. If your canner has a weight only, after about 15 minutes very gently bump the weight with your finger. If it spits any steam, let it cool longer, then try again. If the weight does not hiss at all, carefully remove the weight and set it aside. Loosen the lid and lift it off away from you so if there is any steam it doesn't burn your face or arms.

Using a jar lifter, carefully remove the jars from the canner and place them on a folded towel on your counter or table. Don't have any open windows nearby or a kitchen fan blowing on the jars as that could crack them.

If you are using Tattler reusable canning lids, immediately tighten all rings after removing each jar from the hot canner. If using normal lids, do not touch them until they are cool to the touch, often overnight. Don't poke the lids or wipe the jars or lids. Strictly leave them alone or they may not seal.

When the jars have cooled, gently press down on the center of each lid. The lids should be indented and have no give to them at all. If this is so, you can remove the rings, wash the jars with warm soapy water, then dry. Removing the rings will *not* affect the seal, but will help keep the jar lids from rusting in storage.

Any jar that has not sealed should either be re-canned with a new lid or refrigerated and used soon. If it is re-canned, you will process it just the same as if it was done the first time; there are no shortcuts because it was already canned once.

Once canned, this chicken will remain good for years when stored in a dark, cool, dry spot.

To ensure safety from possible bacteria, it is always a good idea to heat each jar's food to boiling temperature (whether boiling or baking) for 10 to 15 minutes after opening, before tasting.

Besides canning "plain" chicken, you can also can up such things as barbecued chicken (chicken dices canned in barbecue sauce instead of broth), chicken stew, Brunswick stew, and chicken à la king. Imagine how handy it is to have these "meals in a jar" in your pantry so you can quickly dump them into a pan, heat them up and serve … all in less than 15 minutes! And, because they're canned, you never have to worry about your freezer going out, a power outage, or the food becoming freezer burned.

You'll find these recipes in my book, *Growing and Canning Your Own Food.*

I am in the middle of our chicken harvest right now. We raised 15 Cornish Rock meat chickens and also have several "extra" roosters.

From the last two chickens that I canned, I got seven half-pints of diced chicken breast, four pints of large breast pieces, and 14 quarts of chicken stew (chicken, broth, carrots, sweet corn, onions, and potatoes). That's 25 meals … all from two chickens!

Quail recipes

By Allen Easterly

Quail are very lean birds, providing anywhere from 3.5 to 6 ounces of all dark meat per bird. Standard-sized Coturnix quail, the most commonly-raised variety for meat and eggs, comes in at the lower end at 3.5 ounces. Bobwhite quail provides about a 6-ounce carcass.

Quail tastes similar to duck but not nearly as strong. It has a delicate flavor and should not be overcooked or the meat will dry out, leaving it with a mealy texture.

Quail nutritional information (1 oz., cooked)

Calories 66
Total Fat 4g
Saturated Fat 1g
Cholesterol 24 mg
Sodium 15 mg
Total Carbohydrate 0g
Sugar 0 g
Protein 7 g

The following are recipes I've collected over the years from various sources. These recipes call for quail that have already been cleaned and dressed.

Fried quail

4 quail
¼ cup flour
1 tsp. salt
⅛ tsp. pepper

Dredge quail with mixture of flour, salt, and pepper. Heat a deep skillet half-filled with fat over high heat. Once fat is boiling, place the quail in the skillet. Brown quail on both sides, then cover skillet and reduce heat. Cook slowly until tender, about 20 minutes, turning once to brown evenly.

Serves two.

Allen's easy quail

4 quail
jar or can of your favorite gravy
2 cups prepared rice (optional)

Put quail in a small crockpot and pour your favorite jar or can of gravy over the birds (chicken, turkey, or mushroom gravy all work well). Cover and cook on high for about an hour or until meat begins to fall from bone. Can be served over a bed of rice. Serves two.

Quick roasted quail

quail
2 slices bacon per bird

Wrap each bird in bacon and pin with toothpicks. Roast at 400° F for 20 minutes. Serve with any sauce or garnish normally used with chicken. Also good cooked on the grill!

Quail and artichoke casserole

6-8 quail, split down back
6 Tbsp. butter or margarine, divided
paprika
16 oz. artichoke hearts
½ lb. mushrooms
2 Tbsp. flour
⅔ cups chicken broth
3 Tbsp. cream sherry

Melt 4 Tbsp. of the butter in a large pan. Place quail, skin down, in pan and brown on both sides. Place quail in a large, deep casserole dish and sprinkle with paprika. Place artichoke hearts between quail. Add the remaining 2 Tbsp. butter to pan and sauté mushrooms until just browned. Add the flour to pan; stir and add chicken broth gradually, stirring constantly. Cook for a few minutes, then stir in sherry. Salt and pepper to taste. Pour mushrooms and gravy over quail. Cover casserole and bake at 350° F for 1 hour or until fork tender. Serves three to four.

Skewered quail

2 whole quail per person
cabbage leaf for each bird
melted butter with favorite herb(s) added
salt

Brush outside of birds lightly with butter. Use one to two birds per skewer. Wrap each bird in a cabbage leaf and tie it on with a piece of string. Place skewers three to five inches from coals and turn frequently. Cook birds 12-15 minutes. Unwrap birds and brush with melted

Fried quail is delicious and simple. Photo taken by Stewart Butterfield.

butter several times while browning for three to five minutes. Salt birds after cooking.

Quail over rice

6 quail
6 Tbsp. butter
3 Tbsp. flour
2 cups chicken broth
½ cup sherry
salt & pepper to taste
3 oz. chopped mushrooms
6 oz. long grain wild rice, cooked

Brown quail in butter. Remove to baking dish. Add flour to butter. Stir well. Slowly add broth, sherry, salt, and pepper. Blend thoroughly and add mushrooms. Pour over quail. Cover and bake at 350° F for 1 hour. Serve over prepared rice. Serves six.

Quail dressing

1½ cup dry bread crumbs
⅓ tsp. dried savory
1½ cup finely-chopped celery
⅓ tsp. salt
½ onion, finely cut
⅛ tsp. powdered rosemary
⅓ tsp. poultry seasoning
⅓ cup broth or water
1 egg

Combine ingredients and lightly pack into quail (sufficient for six to eight birds), then proceed with cooking directions as outlined in recipe.

Quail eggs

Quail eggs are considered a delicacy and have been prized as a healing food. While quail eggs are small, they are an abundant source of trace elements and vitamins. Their nutritional value is three to four times higher than that of chicken eggs. They provide 13% of proteins, while chicken eggs only provide about 11%. Quail eggs contain more vitamin B1 and twice as much vitamins A and B2 than chicken eggs. Quail eggs provide five times as much iron and potassium than chicken eggs. They also are richer in phosphorus and calcium. Due to their amazing content, quail eggs are considered a dietary food. They do not contain "bad" cholesterol (LDL) and are very rich in "good" (HDL) cholesterol. Unlike chicken eggs, they do not cause allergies. They can actually help fight allergy symptoms due to the ovomucoid protein that is even used in the production of some anti-allergy drugs.

Quail eggs can be used as substitutes for chicken eggs in any recipe at the rate of five standard-sized quail eggs (or three giant-sized quail eggs) for one large chicken egg.

Hard boiling and peeling quail eggs

To make hard boiled quail eggs, place eggs in cool water with a pinch of salt and bring to a light boil. Turn off heat and let sit for five minutes. Stir frequently to prevent yolks from settling to one side. Pour off hot water and cool in cold water. The eggs peel easier when they are about one week old before cooking. To peel, roll egg on a hard surface to crack it all over the shell. Pinch a piece of the shell off the fat end and then peel the rest of the fat end. Peel a strip down the side and across the pointy end. Then just unwrap the egg. As an option to peeling, the shell can be dissolved in full strength vinegar for about 12 hours, agitating every several hours. This still leaves the egg enclosed in a skin-like membrane. The skins can then be removed easily by hand, washed in clean water, and canned, pickled, or refrigerated.

Hard boiled quail eggs taste just like bite-sized chicken eggs. They make delicious appetizers and snacks, or they can be used to dress up salads. They can be pickled (following standard canning procedures) by adding hot, white vinegar (diluted to taste), salt and pepper, and such things as bacon bits, Polish sausage, or hot peppers for flavor. Let stand for 24 to 48 hours before serving. Here are a few ideas on how to use hard boiled eggs.

1. Peeled: dipped in sea salt and eaten with a drink.

2. Coat eggs with lemon mayonnaise (approx. 6 eggs per person). Serve on a bed of salad.

3. Heat eggs in cheese sauce. Sprinkle with cheese and brown under the grill.

4. Heat eggs in curry sauce and serve with rice.

Miniature scotch eggs

quail eggs, hard boiled and shelled
sausage meat
flour
bread crumbs

Coat eggs in flour and wrap in sausage meat, then coat in bread crumbs. Deep fry for a few minutes.

Fancy pickled quail eggs

3 Tbsp. tarragon vinegar
1½ cups mild vinegar
1 Tbsp. pickling spices
2 medium-sized pieces of ginger root
½ tsp. salt
12 hard boiled quail eggs

Place vinegars, spices, and salt together in a pan and simmer all ingredients for 15 minutes. Place shelled eggs in a bowl and completely cover with the pickling solution. When the eggs and mixture have cooled, cover the bowl and place it in a refrigerator for at least 24 hours. Food coloring may be added to the pickling solution as desired.

Rendezvous Farm appetizers

12 large mushroom caps
1 or 2 slices bacon
12 raw quail eggs

Wash and gently remove stem from large mushroom caps; drain. Slice bacon into matchstick size pieces and brown in sauté pan; drain. Arrange a few pieces of bacon in each mushroom cap. Break a quail egg on top of the bacon in each mushroom cap; salt and pepper to taste. Bake at 375° F until whites are cooked and yolks are done to your taste (good runny or hard). The best method of breaking quail eggs is to carefully cut the shell around the middle with a paring knife rather than breaking them on the edge of pan.

When turkey takes over the kitchen

By Habeeb Salloum

Probably one of the most tantalizing aromas that come out of the kitchen is that of a turkey with stuffing roasting in the oven. The traditional roasted turkey can be stuffed in numerous ways. I enjoy traditional bread stuffing but what I truly crave is rice stuffing — the most common of all stuffings for fowl in the Middle East.

Rice-stuffed turkey contains rice enhanced with almonds, a variety of spices, seasonings, and other condiments. On any festive occasion, especially Thanksgiving and Christmas, rice-stuffed turkey serves as a special main dish; a traditional meal with a striking twist.

Regardless what stuffing you use, when everyone has eaten more than their fill, there is the question of what to do with the leftover turkey. Turning what remains into tasty dishes is quite simple. One can eat for some time after on gourmet dishes made from turkey leftovers.

Rice-stuffed turkey

Serves 12

This stuffing can be used for fowl, breasts of lamb, or veal.

1 12-lb. turkey, cleaned, washed, and patted dry
4 Tbsp. lemon juice
3 tsp. salt, divided
½ cup melted butter, divided
½ lb. beef sausage, cut into small pieces
3 medium onions, finely chopped
4 cloves garlic, crushed
4 Tbsp. finely-chopped cilantro leaves
1 hot pepper, seeded and finely chopped
2½ cups hot water, divided
1½ cups white rice, rinsed
½ cup dried cranberries
½ cup blanched almonds, slightly toasted
1 tsp. dried rosemary, divided
1 tsp. ground sage, divided
1 tsp. dried thyme, divided
1 tsp. black pepper, divided
1 tsp. cinnamon, divided
1 tsp. ground ginger, divided
4 Tbsp. liquid honey

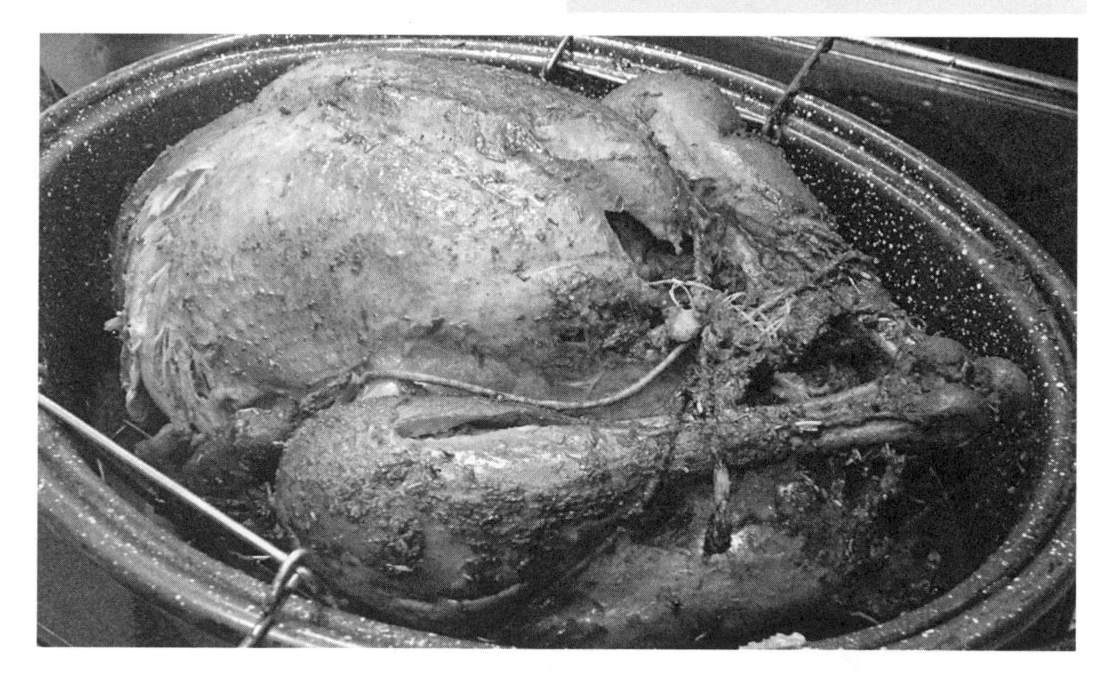

Turkey pot pie

Rub turkey inside and out with a mixture of the lemon juice and 2 tsp. of the salt, then set aside.

In a saucepan, melt 4 Tbsp. of the butter, then sauté sausage over medium heat for 5 minutes. Add onions, garlic, coriander (cilantro) leaves, and hot pepper, then sauté for further 8 minutes. Add remaining 1 tsp. of salt, 1½ cups of the water, rice, cranberries, almonds, rosemary, and half of the following: sage, thyme, pepper, cinnamon, and ginger. Thoroughly mix to complete the stuffing.

Bring to a boil then turn heat to low. Cover then simmer for 10 minutes. Remove from the heat then allow to cool before stuffing turkey.

Stuff turkey including the neck, then sew openings. Pour ½ cup of the water into the roaster then place the turkey in it.

Make a basting by combining the remaining ½ cup hot water, sage, thyme, pepper, cinnamon, ginger, and remaining butter then baste the turkey and cover.

Bake covered in a 325°F preheated oven for 2½ hours, basting every 30 minutes, then turn turkey over. Baste and bake covered for further 2½ hours or until turkey is well-cooked. Mix honey with a little (about 2 Tbsp.) boiling water and baste turkey, then bake uncovered for 10 minutes.

Place stuffed turkey on a serving platter and serve with its stuffing and side dishes as well as the pan juices as gravy.

Bread stuffing

7 cups toasted croutons
2 medium onions, finely chopped and sautéed lightly in butter until limp and just starting to brown
2 cups chopped roasted chestnuts
1 cup chopped fresh parsley or 1 Tbsp. dried parsley
1 cup butter, melted
2 tsp. ground sage
1½ tsp. dried rosemary
1½ tsp. salt
1 tsp. black pepper
1 tsp. cinnamon
1 tsp. dried savory
½ tsp. dried thyme
½ tsp. marjoram
¼ tsp. cayenne
1 cup water

Mix all ingredients well then stuff the turkey as in previous recipe.

Basting for bread-stuffed turkey

Use to baste turkey every 30 minutes.

4 Tbsp. olive oil
1 tsp. ground sage
1 tsp. ground rosemary
2 tsp. salt
1 tsp. paprika
1 tsp. ginger
1 tsp. cinnamon
1 tsp. pepper
½ cup water

Mix all ingredients together well and baste according to directions.

Turkey pot pie

Makes one 9x9-inch pie.

Pie crust:
2½ cups flour
1 Tbsp. baking powder
½ tsp. salt
1 cup butter, softened at room temperature
1 egg, beaten
1 Tbsp. vinegar
2 Tbsp. ice-cold water

Turkey soup

Turkey and pomegranate open-faced sandwich

Turkey-vegetable one-pot dish

Combine all the dry ingredients in a mixing bowl and set aside. In another small bowl, combine the remaining ingredients, then pour a little at a time of this mixture into dry ingredients and knead into dough, adding a little water or milk if needed. Divide dough into two balls, one a little larger, cover with plastic wrap, then refrigerate for 30 minutes.

Filling for the pie:
2 Tbsp. butter
1 medium onion, finely chopped
2 cups cooked turkey, diced into ½-inch cubes
1½ cups fresh or frozen corn, thawed
1½ cups fresh or frozen peas, thawed
1 cup chicken broth
½ cup whipping cream
4 Tbsp. flour dissolved in ½ cup of milk
1 tsp. dried thyme
½ tsp. salt
½ tsp. black pepper
½ tsp. nutmeg
⅛ tsp. cayenne

Preheat oven to 375° F.

Roll out the larger ball of dough to about ⅛-inch thickness and use it to line a 9x9-inch greased casserole dish and set aside.

In a frying pan, melt the butter over medium heat and sauté the onion for 8 minutes. Remove from heat and set aside.

Thoroughly combine all the filling ingredients, including the onions, then pour into the casserole dish.

Roll out the remaining ball of dough to top the pie filling. Pinch edges and cover the fluted edges with strips of tin foil. Bake 50 minutes or until the pie turns golden brown. Serve hot.

Turkey soup

Serves 6

This delicious, hearty soup is a meal in itself that is packed with great flavors.

5 Tbsp. olive oil
1 medium onion, finely chopped
1 medium parsnip, peeled and chopped into ¼-inch pieces
1 medium potato, peeled, and chopped into ¼-inch pieces
½ cup finely-chopped fresh cilantro
1 tsp. ground sage
1 tsp. dried thyme
5 cups turkey or chicken broth
1 cup fresh or frozen peas
1½ tsp. salt
1 tsp. black pepper
3 Tbsp. tomato paste, dissolved in 3 cups of warm water
2 cups cooked and finely-chopped turkey meat (any kind)

In a saucepan, heat oil over medium heat. Add onion and sauté for 5 minutes. Add the parsnip, potato, and cilantro, then cook for 5 minutes over medium/low heat, stirring often. Stir in sage, thyme, and broth, then bring to boil. Cover and lower heat to medium/low and cook for 30 minutes. Add the remaining ingredients and cook covered over medium heat for 20 minutes. Serve hot.

Turkey and pomegranate open-faced sandwich

Makes 8 open-faced sandwiches

- 2 cups cooked turkey, diced into small pieces
- 1 cup pomegranate seeds
- 1 large sweet green bell pepper, seeded and finely chopped
- ½ cup finely-chopped green onion
- ½ avocado, finely chopped
- ½ cup mayonnaise
- 2 Tbsp. lemon juice
- 4 Tbsp. extra-virgin olive oil
- ¾ tsp. salt
- ½ tsp. pepper
- 8 slices sandwich bread

Combine all the ingredients thoroughly, and spread on bread as an open-faced sandwich for an appetizer or for a light lunch. Whole wheat bread adds a great flavor to this delicious spread.

Turkey loaf

Serves 6

A spicy and juicy turkey loaf best served with dill pickles to add that extra punch.

- 2 cups ground cooked turkey
- 3 eggs, beaten
- 1 medium sweet red bell pepper, seeded and finely chopped
- 1 small onion, finely chopped
- ½ cup fine bread crumbs
- 4 Tbsp. tomato paste mixed with 4 Tbsp. olive oil
- 4 Tbsp. ketchup
- 1 tsp. salt
- 1 tsp. dried thyme
- 1 tsp. black pepper
- ½ tsp. ground sage
- ½ tsp. dried rosemary
- ½ tsp. garam masala

Turkey and potato pie

Preheat oven to 350°F.

In a mixing bowl, combine all the ingredients thoroughly together. Pour into a well-greased bread loaf pan. Bake uncovered for 1¼ hours. Remove from oven and let sit for 5 minutes before inverting the loaf onto a serving plate.

Turkey and mushroom casserole

Serves 6

- 2 cups cooked turkey, cut into small pieces
- 2 cups cooked white rice
- 1 small sweet red pepper, seeded and finely chopped
- 1 small onion, finely chopped
- 2 cups sliced small mushrooms
- 1 can (10¾-oz.) condensed cream of mushroom soup
- ½ tsp. garlic powder
- ½ tsp. salt
- ½ tsp. black pepper
- ½ tsp. garam masala

Preheat oven to 350° F.

Combine all ingredients in a greased casserole then cover. Bake 30 minutes then uncover and bake for a further 30 minutes. Serve hot from the casserole.

Turkey-vegetable one-pot dish

Serves about 6

- 4 Tbsp. olive oil
- 4 cups shredded cabbage
- 1 large onion, finely chopped
- 1 medium red bell pepper, seeded and finely chopped
- 2½ cups cooked turkey, chopped
- 1 cup turkey or chicken gravy
- 1 cup chopped parsley
- 2 Tbsp. finely-chopped fresh coriander (cilantro) leaves
- 1 tsp. salt
- ½ tsp. black pepper
- 1 cup water

Heat the oil in saucepan then sauté cabbage, onion, and bell pepper over medium heat until limp. Stir in remaining ingredients and simmer over medium/low heat for 20 minutes. Serve hot.

Turkey corn chili

Turkey and potato pie

Serves 6 to 8

- 3 cups shredded cooked turkey
- 4 Tbsp. butter
- 1 large onion, finely chopped
- 2 cups fresh or frozen green peas
- 1½ cups condensed cream of mushroom soup
- ½ lb. shredded cheddar or similar cheese
- 4 cups mashed potatoes mixed with 1 tsp. salt and ½ tsp. pepper

Preheat the oven to 350° F.

Spread turkey evenly on the bottom of a 9x13-inch greased casserole dish and set aside.

Melt the butter in a frying pan, then fry the onion over medium heat. Spread the fried onions over the top of the turkey. Spread peas over the onion, then pour the condensed soup over the peas.

Mix shredded cheese with the mashed potatoes, and spread evenly over the contents of the casserole and bake uncovered for 40 minutes. Serve hot from casserole.

Turkey corn chili

Serves 6 to 8

- 1 cup dried red or white kidney beans, soaked overnight in water mixed with 1 tsp. baking soda, then drained
- 7 cups water
- 4 Tbsp. olive oil
- 1 large onion, finely chopped
- 6 cloves garlic, crushed
- ½ cup finely-chopped fresh coriander (cilantro) leaves
- 1 lb. ground cooked turkey
- 2 cups fresh or frozen corn
- 3 cups stewed tomatoes
- 1 tsp. chili powder
- 1 tsp. paprika
- 1 tsp. dried thyme
- 1 tsp. ground cumin
- 1½ tsp. salt
- 1 tsp. black pepper

Place beans and water in a saucepan and bring to boil. Cover and cook over medium heat for 1 hour.

In the meantime, heat the oil in a frying pan and fry the onions over medium heat for 6 minutes then add the garlic, coriander (cilantro) leaves, and turkey and stir-fry for 3 minutes. Add frying pan contents to the beans and bring to a boil. Cook covered over medium heat for another 30 minutes. Stir in remaining ingredients, bring to a boil then cook covered over medium heat for another 30 minutes, stirring a few times and adding more water if necessary. Serve immediately.

Cornish hen recipes

By Allen Easterly

Since Cornish hens (sometimes called Cornish game hens) are just young chickens, just about any chicken recipe is appropriate for Cornish hens. Since they are so young, they are considered to be an all white-meat bird. The most significant difference in recipes will be cooking times.

Cornish hen nutritional information, (110g, cooked, roasted half-bird)

Calories 147
Total Fat 4.3 g
Saturated Fat 1.1 g
Cholesterol 117 mg
Sodium 69 mg
Carbohydrates 0 g
Dietary Fiber 0 g
Sugars 0 g

Rendezvous Farm game hens

4 farm-raised Cornish hens
salt and pepper to taste
lemon juice
olive oil

Preheat oven to 450° F. Rinse the hens well, inside and out. Pat thoroughly dry. Season the cavities of the birds with salt and pepper and a squeeze of lemon juice. Truss the birds. Rub them all over with olive oil. Place the birds in a roasting pan with plenty of room between them, and roast until they turn pale gold, about 30 minutes. Check them frequently, and when they begin to give up fat and juices, use these to baste them, basting every 10-15 minutes. Reduce heat to 350 and continue roasting until the birds are deep golden in color and their juices run clear when the thigh and leg joint are pricked with a sharp knife. This will take 10 minutes for one-pound birds and about 20 minutes for larger birds (if cooking less than four birds, less cooking time is needed, so keep a close eye on bird color and juice flow to determine appropriate cooking time.)

No matter what recipe you use, Cornish hens are tender, juicy, white meat delicacies.

Cornish game hens with egg and sausage stuffing

4 farm-raised Cornish hens
1 lb. ground pork sausage
1 tsp. fennel seeds
salt and pepper, to taste
¼ cup finely-chopped parsley
1 Tbsp. finely-chopped fresh sage
4 Tbsp. unsalted butter, divided
1 leek, thinly sliced
1 cup thinly-sliced celery
20 quail eggs or 4 free range chicken eggs, whisked

Preheat oven to 425° F. Brown the sausage with the fennel seeds, breaking the meat into small pieces. Season with salt, pepper, parsley, and sage. Pour into bowl and set aside. Melt 1 to 2 Tbsp. butter in pan, add leek and celery and sauté until veggies begin to soften. Add the eggs and scramble. Mix eggs with sausage. Stuff each bird with the egg and meat mix. Pull the flaps of fat at the tail end of the hens over the open cavity and skewer closed with a toothpick. Pin wing tips to sides of bird with a toothpick. Place birds in a rack or roasting pan so they are not touching each other. Melt 2 Tbsp. butter and brush birds with the melted butter and season with salt and pepper, to taste. Roast about an hour until a meat thermometer inserted through the thigh or breast and into the center of stuffing reaches 165 degrees.

Sausage-stuffed Cornish hens

¼ lb. pork sausage
½ cup sliced mushrooms
1 cup Stove Top Stuffing Mix for Chicken (in the canister)
2 Tbsp. shredded carrots
½ cup hot water
2 farm-raised Cornish hens
1 Tbsp. olive oil
2 Tbsp. apple jelly

Preheat oven to 350° F. Brown sausage with mushrooms in large skillet; drain. Return to skillet. Add stuffing mix, carrots, and hot water; stir just until moistened. Spoon stuffing mix evenly into hen cavities; close openings with skewers (toothpicks work well). Place hens breast-side up in shallow roasting pan. Brush with oil. Bake one hour; spoon jelly over hens. Bake an additional 10 minutes or until thermometer inserted through breast into center of bird reads 180 degrees.

Chicken dishes from North Africa

By Habeeb Salloum

B*astilla* is an exquisite dish made from crispy, paper-thin pastry stuffed with chicken (or pigeon) and almonds. Considered to be the most sophisticated and elaborate of the many Moroccan dishes, this is the crown jewel of the Moroccan kitchen.

Bastilla (pronounced "basteela") has at least six different variations in the spelling alone: *Bastilla, Bestilla, B'steeya, Bisteeya, Bistayla,* and *Pastilla.* A sumptuous, delicate, and aromatic pie, it is usually prepared in Morocco on special occasions: the arrival of a special guest, for holidays, during Ramadan, and at weddings.

Even though *Bastilla* is considered to be the epitome of chicken dishes in Morocco, there are dozens of others that can vie with this delicious feast recipe.

Bastilla

Serves 10 to 12

2 medium-sized onions, finely chopped
¾ cup butter, divided
1 Tbsp. grated fresh ginger
1½ tsp. salt
½ tsp. turmeric
½ tsp. pepper
½ tsp. ground coriander seeds
pinch of saffron
1½ lbs. boned cooked chicken, cut into very small pieces
1 cup chicken stock
½ cup finely-chopped parsley
4 eggs, beaten
1 cup blanched almonds, roasted and ground
3 Tbsp. sugar, divided
12 sheets filo dough
½ tsp. cinnamon

Place the onions, 4 tablespoons of the butter, and ginger in a saucepan, then sauté over medium heat until onions begin to brown. Add salt, turmeric, pepper, coriander, saffron,

Bastilla

chicken pieces, and chicken stock, then cook over medium/low heat for 10 minutes. Add parsley, then cook for further 5 minutes, adding more water if saucepan contents become too thick. Stir in eggs, then stir-fry until eggs are cooked. Remove from the heat and set aside.

Make a filling by mixing half the almonds, 2 tablespoons of the sugar, and the chicken mixture, then set aside.

Melt remainder of butter then set aside.

Place 5 sheets of the filo dough with the sides folded in on the bottom of a greased 9x13-inch pan, brushing each sheet with butter. Spread chicken filling evenly over dough in pan then cover with 5 more sheets of filo dough with sides folded in, brushing each with butter. Spread the remaining almonds evenly over top and cover with the remaining 2 sheets of dough, brushing each sheet heavily with butter and tucking in the edges.

Spread remaining butter over top, then bake in a 350° F preheated oven for 50 minutes or until top begins to turn golden brown. Remove from oven, then sprinkle with remaining 1 tablespoon of sugar and cinnamon. Serve while warm.

Lemon and olive chicken stew (*Tajine Mseer and Zaytoon*)

Serves from 4 to 6

Almost all types of couscous reach their epitome in Morocco.

4 Tbsp. olive oil
3 lbs. chicken, cut into serving-sized pieces
2 medium onions, chopped
6 cloves garlic, crushed
1½ tsp. salt
1 tsp. paprika
1 tsp. ground ginger
1 tsp. pepper
½ tsp. turmeric
2 Tbsp. lemon juice
3 cups water
½ cup green olives, pitted and sliced in half
1 lemon, peeled and sliced thinly

Heat oil in a saucepan; then sauté the chicken over medium heat until it begins to turn light brown, turning the pieces over a few times. Remove chicken pieces with slotted spoon and set aside.

Sauté onions in same oil, adding a little more oil if necessary, over medium/low heat for 10 minutes, then add chicken pieces and stir in remaining ingredients, except olives and lemon slices. Bring to a boil, then turn heat to low and cover. Simmer for about 1½ hours or until chicken is well-done, adding more water if necessary, then add olives and simmer for a further 5 minutes. Remove chicken pieces with a slotted spoon and arrange in the middle of a platter, then place lemon slices in a ring around chicken pieces. Pour sauce over chicken pieces, then serve hot.

Chicken and almond couscous

Serves about 10 to 12

The flavors of the chicken, chickpeas, raisins, and almonds blend well to create a succulent dish.

2 cups couscous
2 large onions, sliced
½ cup olive oil
4 lbs. chicken, cut into serving pieces
4 cups cooked chickpeas
½ cup raisins, rinsed
1 cup lightly-toasted blanched almonds
3 tsp. salt
1 tsp. pepper
1 tsp. cinnamon
1 tsp. ground coriander seeds
½ tsp. turmeric
½ tsp. nutmeg
¼ tsp. ground cloves
7 cups water
4 Tbsp. butter
½ tsp. paprika

Soak couscous in warm water for a few seconds, then quickly drain and place in the top part of the couscousiére or double boiler with a perforated top. Thoroughly break up the lumps in the couscous and set aside.

In the bottom part of the couscousiére or double boiler, place onion and oil, then cook over medium heat for 10 minutes. Add remaining ingredients, except water, butter, and paprika, then stir-fry for about 5 min-

Lemon and olive chicken stew

Chicken and almond couscous

Chicken in garlic

utes. Add water (make sure it generously covers the chicken pieces) and bring to boil. Fit the top part with couscous to the bottom part with stew then seal two parts together with a flour-impregnated piece of cloth. (Should be sealed only if steam is escaping between the two parts.). Cook over medium heat for one hour or until chicken is done, stirring couscous every few minutes to make sure kernels do not stick together. Stir butter into couscous and remove from heat.

Place couscous on a platter pyramid style, then make wide deep well in the middle. With a slotted spoon, remove chicken pieces, chickpeas, raisins, and almonds and place in well. Sprinkle paprika over couscous, then serve. Remaining stew and sauce can be served as a side dish with each person adding extra stew to taste.

Almond, prune, and chicken stew (*Tajine Dajaj bi-Barqooq wa Lawz*)

Serves about 8

Versions of this dish originated in Fez, Morocco.

4 lbs. chicken, cut into serving pieces
3 medium onions, chopped
8 cloves garlic, crushed
½ cup finely-chopped fresh coriander leaves
4 Tbsp. butter
2 tsp. salt
1 tsp. pepper
pinch of saffron
3 cups water
1 cup prunes, pitted
2 Tbsp. honey
1 tsp. cinnamon
½ cup blanched almonds

Place chicken, onions, garlic, coriander, butter, salt, pepper, saffron, and water in a saucepan, then bring to a boil. Cover, then simmer over low heat for about 1½ hours or until the chicken is well done, adding more water if necessary. Remove chicken pieces with a slotted spoon, then place on a platter and keep warm.

Add prunes to the sauce, then simmer over low heat for 10 minutes. Stir in honey and cinnamon, then continuing simmering uncovered for another 10 minutes. Pour sauce over chicken pieces, then decorate with almonds and serve hot.

Chicken in garlic (*Tajine Dajaj*)

Serves about 4

Not as elaborate as the Moroccan tajines, this Libyan chicken stew is nevertheless tasty and wholesome.

- 2 lbs. boneless chicken, cut into small pieces
- 2 Tbsp. tomato paste, diluted in ½ cup water
- 4 Tbsp. olive oil
- 1½ tsp. salt
- 1 tsp. pepper
- 6 cloves garlic, crushed
- ½ tsp. chili powder

Combine all the ingredients in a casserole then marinate for one hour. Cover and place in 350° F preheated oven and bake for one hour. Serve hot from the casserole with cooked rice.

Chicken and vegetable soup (*Shorba Dejej*)

Serves 8 to 10

- 4 Tbsp. olive oil
- 1 lb. chicken, cut into ½-inch cubes
- 1 medium onion, finely chopped
- 4 cloves garlic, crushed
- 4 Tbsp. finely-chopped fresh coriander leaves
- 1 medium potato, diced into ½-inch cubes
- 1 large sweet pepper, cut into small pieces
- 2 cups cooked chickpeas
- 7 cups boiling water
- 1½ tsp. salt
- 1 tsp. pepper
- ½ tsp. cumin
- 1 Tbsp. dried mint
- ¼ cup fine vermicelli, broken
- 2 Tbsp. tomato paste
- ½ cup fresh or frozen peas

Chicken and vegetable soup

Chicken rolls

In a saucepan, heat the oil and sauté chicken over medium heat for 5 minutes. Add onion, garlic, and coriander leaves then sauté for a further 8 minutes. Stir in potato, sweet pepper, chickpeas, and boiling water, then bring to a boil. Cover and lower to medium/low heat and simmer for 50 minutes. Stir in the remainder of the ingredients, then simmer for a further 15 minutes and serve hot.

Chicken rolls (*Bourek Dajaj*)

Makes 12 rolls

12 cooked crepes
4 Tbsp. olive oil
2 cups ground chicken
1 medium onion, finely chopped
1 tsp. lemon zest
½ tsp. *ras al hanout* (spice mix from North Africa)
½ tsp. salt
½ tsp. allspice
4 Tbsp. finely-chopped fresh coriander
2 hard boiled eggs, chopped
4 Tbsp. melted butter, for brushing

Heat the olive oil over medium heat in a frying pan, then add the chicken and onion and sauté for 12 minutes. Stir in the remaining ingredients except for the coriander, hard-boiled eggs, and melted butter. Stir-fry for 2 minutes. Remove from heat, then stir in the coriander and eggs.

Preheat oven to 350° F.

Lay the crepes out on a flat surface. Spoon one heaping tablespoon of the chicken mixture along the bottom half of the crepe, then carefully roll into a cylinder. Place the rolled crepe on a greased baking sheet, seam side down. Continue until all the crepes are rolled. Brush butter lightly all over the tops of the crepes. Bake for 20 minutes then serve immediately.

Chicken peanut stew (*Mafe*)

Serves about 6 to 8

Versions of this Mauritanian dish, prepared throughout West Africa, can be cooked with other type of meats.

2 lbs. chicken legs
4 Tbsp. peanut or olive oil
1 large onion, finely chopped
4 cloves garlic, crushed
3 cups water
4 Tbsp. tomato paste, dissolved in 1 cup boiling water
4 Tbsp. peanut butter, dissolved in ½ cup boiling water
2 cups chopped cabbage
2 cups sweet potato, peeled and diced into ½-inch pieces
2 cups turnips, peeled and diced into ½-inch pieces
1½ tsp. salt
1 tsp. pepper
½ tsp. ground ginger
½ tsp. paprika
¼ tsp. cinnamon
¼ tsp. cayenne pepper
2 Tbsp. chopped roasted peanuts

Heat oil in a saucepan, then fry chicken legs over medium heat for 6 minutes. Stir in onion and garlic and fry for a further 5 minutes, stirring often. Add water, tomato paste, and peanut butter, then bring to boil. Reduce heat to medium low and simmer for 20 minutes. Add remaining ingredients, except peanuts, and cook over low heat for 50 minutes or until chicken and vegetables are done. Garnish with peanuts and serve with cooked rice.

Chicken olive lemon tagine (*Djaj mqualli*)

Serves 4

I enjoyed this dish at La Munia Restaurant in Casablanca, Morocco.

1 chicken, cleaned and washed, then cut into 4 pieces
4 medium onions, chopped
1 cup finely-chopped fresh coriander leaves
1 cup finely-chopped parsley
5 cloves garlic, crushed
¼ cup olive oil
1 tsp. salt
1 tsp. cumin
½ tsp. pepper
½ tsp. ginger
pinch of saffron
1 lemon, quartered
1½ cups green olives, pitted

Place all ingredients except the lemon and olives in a saucepan then thoroughly mix. Sauté over medium heat for 10 minutes. Add just enough water to cover, then cook over medium heat for about 45 minutes or until the chicken is almost done and there is only a small amount of the liquid left. Add the lemon and cook for a further 10 minutes, then stir in the olives and cook for another 5 minutes.

Note: In Morocco, instead of the fresh lemon, a pickled lemon is used. If this is available, add the lemon with the olives, during the last 5 minutes of cooking.

MEET THE AUTHORS

SAMANTHA BIGGERS is the author of *Raising Pastured Pigs* and *Insourcing: Bringing Production Back Into Your Home*, as well as many other books and articles on homesteading. She writes and works from Morning Star Vineyards in the mountains of North Carolina.

JILL BONG is the creator of Chicken Armor hen saddles. They can be purchased on Jill's website at www.chickenarmor.com. She can be contacted through her website.

JACKIE CLAY-ATKINSON and her husband, Will, homestead a 120-acre piece of northern Minnesotan woods, raising at least 80% of their own food. Sharing their homestead are horses, beef cattle, a milk cow, dairy goats, chickens, and turkeys.

KENNY COOGAN, CPBT-KA, has a B.S. in animal behavior and is a certified bird trainer through the International Avian Trainers Certification Board. He is a weekly pet columnist and has authored a children's book titled *A Tenrec Named Trey (And other odd lettered animals that like to play)*. Please search "Critter Companions by Kenny Coogan" on Facebook to learn more.

NELL DAVIDSEN lives on a one-acre homestead in the outskirts of a small Oregon community. She has 10 spoiled chickens that periodically escape and raid her garden. She doesn't have the heart to put any of her chickens in the stew pot, but don't tell them that.

DOTTY DEVILLE is happily retired and lives in a bustling town with her husband, where she enjoys cooking, canning, and tending to her backyard flock of chickens.

ALLEN EASTERLY operates a small hobby farm in the heart of the Shenandoah Valley, in Virginia. He also raises rabbits, quail and squab. Visit his website at www.RendezvousHobbyFarm.com and be sure to "like" RendezvousFarm on Facebook.

KAREN HOUSE lives and writes at her home in the mountains of east Tennessee. She blogs as "Granny Fisher" at www.womaninthewilderness.weebly.com.

DONNA INSCO has lived on a small farm for more than 25 years. She gardens and raises a variety of small livestock.

JAMES KASH is an 18-year-old homesteader from Eastern Kentucky. James raises a variety of poultry on his homestead in the Appalachian Mountains including more than 50 laying hens, four turkeys, two geese, and one lone duck.

KARI KELLEY and her husband were inspired to turn a free dog house into a chicken coop thanks to *Backwoods Home Magazine*. Since 2013, they have been trying to live a more sustainable lifestyle. They currently have three Nigerian Dwarf Goats, 14 chickens, nine ducks, and three turkeys. They hope to raise many other animals in the future.

AMANDA KEMP and her husband Matt write about their adventures in striving for self-sufficiency on a small town lot at www.kempfreehold.com. You can find the first two books in the Kemp Freehold Frugality Series, *Finding Freedom with Frugality* and *Food, Frugality, and Freedom*, on the Amazon Kindle store.

HABEEB SALLOUM is a prominent Arab-Canadian freelance writer. He is considered Canada's foremost expert on Arab cuisine. Currently, he has written seven cookbooks.

CHARLES SANDERS lives on 40 rugged acres in rural Indiana, where he raises beef cattle, grows hay, and tends fruit trees and a large vegetable garden. He is the author of *The Self-Reliant Homestead*, available through *Backwoods Home Magazine*.

MELISSA SOUZA is a homemaker and homeschooling mother of four. Her family works towards improving their modern homestead and bettering their skills to support a lifestyle closer to God, closer to family, and closer to nature. Melissa believes in being useful, aware, and prepared in an ever-changing world.

DAVID A. WILLIAMS homesteads in central Texas and has written two eBook novels available on Kindle: *Strings* (www.amazon.com/dp/B00JFHRZZC) and *Red Oak* (www.amazon.com/dp/B00JFHDZ4W). He also writes and blogs at www.zamtoe.com.

JEANIE WOODBURN is a country gal who likes doing things herself. She lives in northern California with her three dogs and her chicken flock.

Other titles available from Backwoods Home Magazine

The Best of the First Two Years
A Backwoods Home Anthology — The Third Year
A Backwoods Home Anthology — The Fourth Year
A Backwoods Home Anthology — The Fifth Year
A Backwoods Home Anthology — The Sixth Year
A Backwoods Home Anthology — The Seventh Year
A Backwoods Home Anthology — The Eighth Year
A Backwoods Home Anthology — The Ninth Year
A Backwoods Home Anthology — The Tenth Year
A Backwoods Home Anthology — The Eleventh Year
A Backwoods Home Anthology — The Twelfth Year
A Backwoods Home Anthology — The Thirteenth Year
A Backwoods Home Anthology — The Fourteenth Year
A Backwoods Home Anthology — The Fifteenth Year
A Backwoods Home Anthology — The Sixteenth Year
A Backwoods Home Anthology — The Seventeenth Year
A Backwoods Home Anthology — The Eighteenth Year
A Backwoods Home Anthology — The Nineteenth Year
A Backwoods Home Anthology — The Twentieth Year
A Backwoods Home Anthology — The Twenty-first Year
A Backwoods Home Anthology — The Twenty-second Year
A Backwoods Home Anthology — The Twenty-third Year
A Backwoods Home Anthology — The Twenty-fourth Year
Backwoods Home Cooking
Can America Be Saved From Stupid People
Creative Home Improvement
Chickens — a beginner's handbook
Starting Over — Chronicles of a Self-Reliant Woman
Dairy Goats — a beginner's handbook
Self-reliance — Recession-proof your pantry
Making a Living — Creating your own job
Harvesting the Wild: gathering & using food from nature
Growing and Canning Your Own Food
Jackie Clay's Pantry Cookbook
Homesteading Simplified: Living the good life without losing your mind
Ask Jackie: Animals
Ask Jackie: Canning Basics
Ask Jackie: Food Storage
Ask Jackie: Gardening
Ask Jackie: Homestead Cooking
Ask Jackie: Homesteading
Ask Jackie: Pressure Canning
Ask Jackie: Water Bath Canning